REEF
A "Getting to Kn ... ide

Great Barrier Reef Australia
Indonesia Archipelago
Malaysia
Papua New Guinea
Fiji and other South Pacific Islands
Maldives
Micronesia
Thailand
Philippines

Proceeds from this book
contribute to Save Our Seas Fund

OceanNEnvironment

With Tips on Underwater Photography   *Michael AW*

The Indo Australasia Archipelago

Bio-diversity is a term used to describe the richness of flora and fauna of a region. The Indo-Pacific Ocean, extending from the east coast of East Africa and the Red Sea, eastward to French Polynesia and the Northern Pacific shores of Hawaii, is regarded as the world's richest marine province. However, marine scientists unanimously confirm that it is the Indo-Australasian Archipelago, comprising Indonesia, Malaysia, South Thailand the Philippines, Papua New Guinea and Northern Australia, that forms the heart of the region harboring the greatest wealth of marine bio-diversity. To the east as distance increases across the Pacific, richness of fauna progressively decrease. To the west, diversity decreases by about a third and remains constant around the Indian Ocean reefs. Current estimation stands at over 3200 fish species in the Archipelago, 2500 in the Philippines, 1300 in the Australian Great Barrier Reef to about 800 in the Red Sea.

CONTENTS

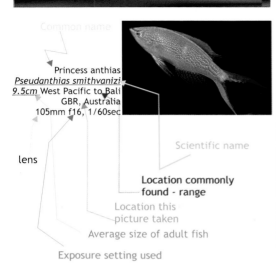

how to use this book

For ease of use, the 37 fish families are placed into 3 colour coded sections. To identify the fish you saw, noting the habitat is very important.

Common name

Princess anthias
Pseudanthias smithvanizi
<u>9.5cm</u> West Pacific to Bali
GBR, Australia
105mm f16, 1/60sec

Scientific name

Location commonly found - range

Location this picture taken

Average size of adult fish

lens

Exposure setting used

BLUE - Fishes found free swimming on reefs, reef slope, walls and the planktonic zone.

Red - fishes that are often found beneath overhangs or usually living in a hole.

Orange -benthic zone, fishes found on the sea bed, ledges, on walls and reef beds

What's in a name?

Scientists use a unique system devised by Carl Linnaeus in the 18th century, to identify organisms in Latin throughout the world. Thus it does not matter which language a book is written is, the species name remains the same. Each name comprises two Latin words and the system is referred to a "binominal nomenclature." A family is composed of fishes that have overall similar characteristics and share a common line of ancestry.

In this book, the respective families are colour coded into section. Next to every picture you will first see a common name, followed by a scientific name.

The scientific name is made up of two words; the first, beginning with a capital letter, refers to the genus - a group of separate species with many similar external and internal features. The second word is in lower case and it is a unique name given to an unique specie.

Example: Rainford's butterflyfish
Chaetontidae: the family of all Butterflyfishes.
Genera: *Chaetodon* closely related butterflyfishes.
Species: *rainford*i - the unique name of the specie.

How to ID fishes:

All fishes possess a few distinguishing characteristics that separate them from one another. Like Sherlock Holms, when trying to identify a fish you saw, you will need a combination of clues. These include where you saw that fish, its size, body shape, distinguishing features, colours, type of fins and especially the shape of their tail crescent or forked. For ease of description on the size of a fish, we suggest that you use the following comparisons.

Tiny - as long as your little finger or less
Small - as long as your hand or less
Medium - as long as your forearm or less
Large - as long as your forearm or bigger
Giant - bigger than you!

Other important clues to look out for:
Shape - is the fish disc shaped / round body / stick-like / torpedo shape
Tail - pedal / fork / elongated
Mouth - long / beaked / curve up / curve down / long snout
Colours - monotone / 2 colours / 3 colours
Distinguishing features stipes - how many? / barbells / whiskers / eye-spot on body
Eyes colours - shape / size relative to body / false eye spot at tail
What was the fish doing?

External Features of Bony Fishes - clues to look out for

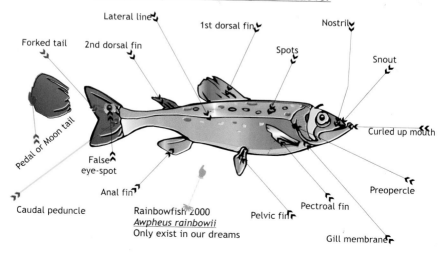

Lateral line
1st dorsal fin
Nostril
Forked tail
2nd dorsal fin
Spots
Snout
Pedal or Moon tail
Curled up mouth
False eye-spot
Anal fin
Preopercle
Caudal peduncle
Rainbowfish 2000
Awpheus rainbowii
Only exist in our dreams
Pelvic fin
Pectroal fin
Gill membrane

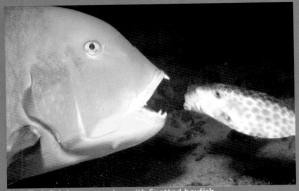

Blue Tusk fish in communion with Spotted boxfish
Navy Pier, Exmouth, W Australia

Author & Photographer : Michael AW
Scientific Editor : Dr. Gerald Allen
Editor : Alison Redhead
Associate Editor : Merridy Cairn-Duff
Art & Graphics : Artistry Unlimited
Printed by : Print Resources

Publisher
OceanNEnvironment Ltd
PO Box 2138, Carlingford Court NSW 2118, Australia
www.OceanNEnvironment.com.au
E-mail: oneocean@OceanNEnvironment.com.au
Fax 61 2 9686 3688

First edition 1994 Ocean Discoverers Michael AW/Laura Woodward
Revised Edition - 2000 Michael AW

National Library of Australia Cataloging in-Publication Entry
Michael AW / Tropical Reef Fishes   A "Getting to Know You" and
Identification Guide

ISBN 0 9587132 6 X

"A human being is part of a whole, called by us the Universe, a part limited in time and space. He experiences himself, his thoughts and feelings, as something separated from the rest--a kind of optical delusion of his consciousness. This delusion is a kind of prison for us, restricting us to our personal desires and to affection for a few persons nearest us. Our task must be to free ourselves from this prison by widening our circles of compassion to embrace all living creatures and the whole of nature in its beauty." - Albert Einstein (1879-1955)

As I was completing the manuscript for this book, a space shuttle had just completed a 3-dimentional photographic shoot of our physical world, a mega million-dollar project. The technology has mapped every mountain, every cliff, every valley in such accuracy that they are able tells the depth of every crack and the shape of every hill on our entire planet. Yet, they can't tell us exactly how many species of fishes there are in the ocean. The cost of the Iraq war was $2.4 billion per day; global budget for military expenditure is $4000 billion per year, a meager sum compare to funds required to protect the world's biodiversity that is estimated to be less than US$600 billion per year. Yet the latter is not even on any agenda. By now every one of us knows that more 70% of Earth's surface is water and that the ocean supports all living beings. But it remained a puzzling question, especially to those of us who recognized the fact that our politicians spend so little resources to protect our one and only ocean. The "out of sight and out of mind" mentality is obvious. If only the ocean was as clear as our sky (well in some places at least), perhaps than we will realize the urgency in cleaning up our act and protect it resources.

In another context, millions of dollars have gone into re-habitating Keiko, the orca made famous by the Hollywood movie "Free Willy". Environmentalists argue that the exercise is only saving one animal and not saving the species. Yes, what about the other animals of the ocean, what about the coral reefs? To protect an endangered species, we have to go beyond protecting one animal, go beyond protecting the species; we have to protect the habitat. Buying our children "Free Willy" merchandise will not save the ocean.

Not long ago I made this observation beneath the Navy Pier, Exmouth, West Australia. Whilst shooting one morning, I saw three Spotted boxfish appearing in front of a Blue-task fish and proceed to yap in a dog-like fashion. In response, the bigger fish chewed up a few barnacles into bits for the boxfish to eat. I don't claim to fully understand the relationship between the boxfish and Blue-tusk fish, but I know that there are many living arrangements in the sea that we have yet to discover. If we were to protect the boxfish, we have to protect the Blue-tusk fish, ultimately the habitat as well. Thus with this book, I am sharing with you my observations that I have made through the years and I hope that it will enhance your affinity with reef fishes and eventually help to preserve our ocean environment.

Understanding, appreciation and love begets preservation and protection.   Michael AW

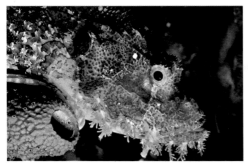
Beared scorpionfish

Besides a few exceptions, generally fishes are recalcitrant models; they are deliberately obstinate and they are masters of the disappearing act. So to make good pictures of fishes, my philosophies are - 1) there is plenty of fishes in the sea (well sometimes) if one is a pain in the bottom, find another one. 2) Patience is of the essence if you absolutely must take a picture of that particular fish remember, sometimes you don't get second chance.

Like an artist, sculptor or dentist, you must have the right tool for the job and shoot a lot to get that 'perfect' shot. The technical aspect of underwater photography must be second nature to you; when you are out there trying to coax a fish into frame, the last thing is your want to do is to fumble with exposure and speed settings. Besides the big animals, all my fish pictures are captured with either the 60mm or 105mm lens in a house camera system. I use the Ikelite S200; it recharges quickly and the spotting light works well as a dive light during night dive. This way, I have my left hand free to re-position the strobe quickly and right hand to work on the trigger.

To be productive, dive with a shooting list; with a few subjects in mind, you would have carried the right lens and go single-mindedly to capture some good pictures. Sure, sometimes we get distracted by the hammerhead who just happens to swim past when you are all set up to shoot gobies and shrimp with a 105mm lens set up. Now you want to cheat a little, you want to increase your odds; the way to do this is to go to places where you are almost certain to find friendly fish, yes, location, location, and location. You must learn the hideouts, the address of your subject don't bother swimming in the blue if you are looking for

Bi-color blenny

Mandarinfish they don't live there. Learn about where fishes live and where fishes play. As far as habitats are concern, you will get many clues in this book.

Okay, you have spotted your subject don't risk scaring them away. Remember, in a fish's perspective, you are an alien with an unfish-like face and most annoyingly you exhale noisy bubbles. No wonder fishes run away from you, I would too. Take time to watch and stalk their movements; most fishes have a range and they nearly always come back to an approximate spot. Remember, you want to get up close and personal; you want to frame the entire fish or a close up profile keep it simple and get really close. Also remember the ONE principle one light source, one film and one message technique. I use Velvia exclusively.

It is also necessary to have a bonding period; assure the fish that you are here to make them famous. Try 'talking' to your subject. Talk to them from heart it

Yellow boxfish - juv.

works. Expose a few frames to get them acquainted with the flash. Take your time to watch, learn about their behavior and traits. Once you have their trust, you can most often move in for the shot, but approach with the dexterity of a cat and be prepared to take a step back, to assure that you are not a threat. But also remember, like you and me, fish have personality too and each one of them is a thinking fish. Slight behavior varies from individual to individual. Great Pictures take time.

For your benefit, alongside each picture, I have given you my exposure setting and the lens used. You may wish to join me sometime in a photographic expedition. I will share with you more secrets but really they are all common sense.

Most importantly, enjoy shooting.

Best fishes

Square spot anthias -female

Known to marine scientists as *Cheilinus undulatus*, Napoleon Wrasse is the biggest of the of the wrasse family and may weigh up to 180 kg. Those knowledgeable with their growth rates calculate that a fish of such size could realistically be a century old. Napoleon wrasse are now under threat from extinction because of the lucrative demand for live Napoleons in Asia. Unscrupulous traders finance illegal operations to harvest this fish with cyanide in Indonesia, the Philippines and most of the Indo-Pacific region. Besides threatening extinction of this gregarious animal, they are also destroying the remaining coral reefs of the world.

In some instances, 55-gallon drums are simply launched onto the reef, turning the area into an aquatic graveyard as the chemical kills corals, invertebrates and non-targeted fish indiscriminately. In 1995, nearly two-thirds of the live fish that were sold in restaurants in Taiwan, Hong Kong and Singapore, which amounted to approximately 25,000 tons valued at US one billion dollars, were captured with sodium cyanide. According to reports from the WWF, over 6,000 cyanide divers squirt an estimated 150,000 kg of dissolved poison on some 33 million coral heads annually. If the current demand of the live reef fish trade imposed on Napoleon Wrasse is allowed to continue, extinction is imminent. Even without the pressures of the live reef fish trade, Napoleon Wrasse are by no means found in abundance in the wild. The Napoleon wrasse is currently listed by the International Union for the Conservation of Nature and Natural Resources (IUCN) Red List as a threatened species being adversely impacted by increased human activities that in future is susceptible of becoming critically endangered or extinct.

Whilst we cannot protect all the animals in the wild, we *can* protect and watch out for those known remaining populations. Protection of this species will further the development of eco-tourism activities that will facilitate interaction with these large charismatic animals in the wild. Experiencing a close encounter with one of these underwater royals a thousand times over by divers is a stark contrast to the commercial reality of selling an individual fish once it reaches the wholesaler. For this reason, OceanNEnvironment, in collaboration with scientists in the Indo-Pacific region, has developed NAPWATCH, the Napoleon Wrasse International Monitoring Program.

These markings are unique.

Humphead wrasse facial markings are unique, much like fingerprints. If you see a Napoleon wrasse, send us a note on facial characteristics, linked to a graphics-supporting database. OceaNEnvironment will be able to track re-sights of individuals over time, and estimate population sizes. It will also be able to track the 'disappearance' of known individuals. Also include: time, location, size, behavior, your name and contact details. **Download Napwatch form from** www.OceanNEnvironment.com.au

HOW YOU CAN HELP:

1. Join our NapWatch member program.

2. Help us document the remaining numbers of Napoleon wrasse in the wild by reporting your sightings to NapWatch. The information that is required for the database includes: specific location of the fish (time, depth, location of reef), number of individuals in each group, description of size and distinctive facial markings. The database will be the primary instrument with which OceanNEnvironment will lobby for total protection of the species in the region, as well as to assist marine scientists with information on behavior, density and distribution of Napoleon Wrasse.

3. Do NOT patronize restaurants that serve Napoleon wrasse and discourage others from doing so.

NAPWATCH MEMBER
ONLY A\$ 35 PA WILL HELP SAVE NAPOLEON WRASSE
BENEFITS:
1. Listed in OceanNEnvironment's NapWatch Supporter Roll
2. Certificate of Appreciation
3. 10 % discount on all OceanNEnvironemt's merchandise and expeditions.
4. OneOcean Portrait Book value at A\$25

For more information e-mail or Fax: 61 2 9686 3688
oneocean@OceanNEnvironment.com.au
Send us your Name, address, email address, postal address with A\$35 cheque or credit card information with expiry date and we will send you a membership package.

OceanNEnvironment Ltd
A Non-Profit Organisation for the Ocean Environment
www.OceanNEnvironment.com.au
PO Box 2138, Carlingford Court Post Office
Carlingford, NSW 2118, Australia

Belonging to a unique group of fishes, the common features of sharks and rays are their hardened cartilaginous skeleton and for reproduction involving internal fertilization. Sharks are similar to bony fishes with their pectoral fins separate from the sides of head, while rays are fused to the sides of the head, over the gills. Rays are disc shape, and sharks are uniquely shark shaped. Scientifically, cartilaginous fishes are classified in 43 families, about 350 species of sharks and 500 rays.

Getting to Know SHARKS

The mention of the word shark is enough to send shivers running down the spines of most people. Myths, superstition and the movies have ensured that the public retains the image of a shark as a man-eating, ferocious and savage predator. Although shark attacks are real only a few species are known to have attacked human under ambiguous circumstances. Out of the 350 species, only a few species are known to have caused injury. Among the earliest in evolution, they have been around for more than 400 million years. Everyone is familiar with the shape of the shark. It is typically cigar shaped in shades of grey and silver with a long pointed elongated snout, pair of obvious nostrils, numerous sharp conspicuous teeth, large pectoral fins and that famous pointed upright dorsal fin or fin. Shape and size varies for each species as does their habitat and mode of sociability. Sharks have coarse denticles instead of scales and their skeleton is made of cartilage instead of bone.

Reef sharks

Reef sharks that you are most likely to see swimming around the outer reefs or resting beneath ledges or in caves are the Blacktip (*Carcharhinus melanopterus*), Whitetip *(Triaendon obesus)*, Leopard shark (*Stegostoma fasciatum*) and Nurse shark (Ginglymostomatidae). **The Blacktip shark and Whitetip reef shark** are easily identified by their respective black or white tip on the dorsal, caudal, pelvic and pectoral fins. Both feed mainly on fishes but supplement their diet with crustaceans and are considered harmless. The Blacktip shark reaches a length of 2.5m(8ft) whilst the more slender Whitetip reaches a maximum size of 2.1m(7ft) and tends to be more curious often-approaching divers at close range. Both have small litters of about 10 pups.**The Leopard shark**, so called because of its spots, has a large dorsal fin with a smaller second one and an extremely long rounded caudal fin. Grey to yellow brown with spots with a common size of 150-250cm (5-8ft), Leopard sharks are slow swimmers and generally considered a passive animal. **Nurse sharks** can be recognised by their two equal-sized dorsal fins and barbells on the chin (whiskers) and can often be seen cruising around the bottom in search of food, with their mouth and barbells close to the ground. Their diet includes mainly fishes crabs, lobsters, and other crustaceans. They are generally considered to be harmless but may bite and inflict serious injury if provoked.

Diet: planktonic food source including small crustacean, squids and fishes.

Whale sharks
Rhincodon typus
12m Indo-Pacific
may grow to 18m, it is the world's largest fish
Exmouth, Australia
16mm f11 1/125sec

Diet: live fish

Silvertip shark
Carcharhinus albimarginatus
3m Indo-Pacific
Burma Banks
24mm f8 1/125sec

Diet: shellfishes, crabs and shrimps.

Leopard shark
Stegostoma fasciatum
3m E Africa to Australia
GBR, Australia
28mm f8, 1/60sec

Eat or Be Eaten

Sharks are flesh eaters and nocturnal hunters feeding mainly on fishes, crustaceans and molluscs. Contrary to belief however, it is not human flesh that forms part of their diet. They possess good eyesight, an excellent sense of smell and a good set of teeth, often with serrated teeth in the fish-eating species designed for seizing and tearing their prey. They also have the finely tuned ability to detect low frequency vibrations at considerable distances. This enables the detection of prey from a distance, such as the electric field surrounding a sleeping or sick fish, and in turn acts as an early warning system against predators. Sharks are garbage removers of the sea. Its assigned duties are to remove sick fishes that would otherwise spread disease among the other reef communities. Research has shown that a human swimming on the surface emits the same energy signals as a sick fish; hence unprovoked attacks on humans happen at or near the surface, a case of mistaken identity by a shark trying to do their job.

In Bed with Sharks

Sharks differ from other fish in their method of reproduction. Most fish lay pelagic eggs in vast numbers with a low survival rate. In contrast sharks bear only a few young, called pups, but at birth they are fully developed and equipped for survival with the ability to swim and hunt on their own. In some super-shark families, to guarantee survival after birth, the fittest pup actually devours the weaker ones whilst still in the womb of its mother. Likewise, unlike most other fish, in sharks fertilization is internal. After a rough courtship for the female, who is often repeatedly bitten by the male prior to copulation, sexual intercourse involves the male inserting his clasper (a two penis-like appendage) into the female's genital organ. A shark's pregnancy period varies, as does the method of gestation. Ranging from a few months to a few years most mothers carry the developing embryos in their uterus, just like humans, and produce live young. In a few species however, like the Swell *(Scyliorhinidae* sp.), Horn (*Heterodontus sp.*) or Port Jackson (*Heterodontus portusjacksoni)* Sharks the embryos are sealed in leathery egg cases and deposited on the bottom.

Shooting Sharks & Rays

It is not easy to see a shark, let alone photograph them. Most good shark photographs are taken during shark feeds. The best opportunity to photograph sharks without provoking them is on the outer reef, where they are frequently seen cruising the reef or found resting beneath ledges or in crevices. If you are using a Nikonos with a 20mm or 15mm lens you will need to get really close. Rays are easy, i.e. once you get close to them again have the right lens for the job is essential.

Diet: mainly small fishes

Black-tip reef shark
Carcharhinus melanopterus
1.8m, Indo-Pacific
Flores, Indonesia
28mm f11 1/60sec

A female -bite scars
from courtship

Diet: small fishes and crustaceans
Grey Reef shark
Carcharhinus amblyrhynchos
2.55m Indo-Pacific
Ujulang Atoll, Marshall Is.
28mm f8 1/125sec

Diet: Cephalopod & small fishes
White-tip reef shark
Triaenodon obesus
2.1m Indo-Pacific
GBR, Australia
28mm f8, 1/125sec

Diet: Shellfishes & crustaceans
Tawny Nurse shark
Nebrius ferrugineus
3.2 Indian Ocean to W Pacific
Myanmar
28mm f11, 1/60sec

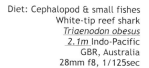

Coral Cat shark
Atelomycterus marmoratus
70cm W. Pacific to Indian Oce
Alor, Indonesia
60mm f11 1/125sec

Tasselled wobbegong
Eucrossohrinus dasypogon
*3.6*m, Northern Australia to Pľ
Exmouth, West Australia
60mm f11, 1/60sec

Blue Spotted ray
Taeniura lymna
*80*cm,Indo-Pacific
GBR, Australia
28mm f11, 1/60sec

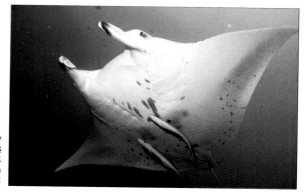

Manta Ray
Manta birostris
<u>7m</u> Circum-tropical
GBR, Australia
60mm f5.6 1/125sec

Blackspotted fantail ray
Taeniura melanospilos
<u>3</u>m, Indian Ocean
Ari Atoll, Maldives
18mm f8, 1/60sec

Spotted eagleray
Aetobatus narinari
<u>250</u>cm, Circumtropical
Kapalai, Malaysia
28mm f11, 1/60sec

We have presented these two families together because they are frequently mistaken for each other. They are both stick-like shape, but Trumpetfishes are only seen during the day whilst Flutemouth or Cornetfish are seen day and night. Trumpetfishes are compressed side to side, while Flutemouths are compressed top to bottom. The two families differ in habitats; Trumpetfishes are characteristically found on most reef environments, whereas Flutemouth are mainly confined to inshore reefs.

Getting to Know Trumpetfishes (Aulostomidae)

A single species family, Trumpetfish (*Aulostomus chinensis*) reaches up to 80cm(36") in length. Active predators of fishes found in tropical and sub-tropical water, they live on the most reef environments. The body of a Trumpetfish is solid, and has a trumpet-like face with a barbell on the chin. Small dorsal and anal fins sit directly above one another near the rounded caudal fin (tail). The pelvic fins are located at the rear of the body and the row of sharp spines on the back is only raised in defense. A slow swimmer, the trumpetfish relies on camouflage and stealth to hunt by ambush sneaking up on a victim by hiding behind the bodies of larger fish or hiding patiently in coral outcrops. Camouflage artists, they are well known for their ability to change colour almost instantly to blend in with the background.

Getting to Know Flutemouths (Fistulariidae)

Flutemouths are elongated fishes with a depressed body, belonging to a single genus family comprising of 4 species, but only the Smooth flutemouth (*Fistularia commersonii*)is commonly sighted. They have a very long tubular snout, with a small oblique mouth at the end. Flutemouth also have small dorsal and anal fins directly above one another but their tail is forked with a long filament, which easily distinguishes them from trumpetfish. When hunting, they search the reef floor for invertebrates and small fishes. They feed by sucking in a pipette-like fashion.

In Bed with Fluties and Trumpeters

Sex for Flutemouths and Trumpetfish maybe a *sticky affair*; they are mid water spawners, releasing eggs and sperms into water column. Very few observations are recorded of their courting behavior, though there was one observation on the Great Barrier Reef. A male was observed weaving back and forth a female with a swollen belly. In an apparent spawning ascent, the female started up with the male still weaving behind her to a height of about 5 to 8 metres before turning back to the bottom. The process was repeated three times, but on the third attempt, the pair made a smooth arc upward, side by side. Gamete was released at the apex.

Shooting Flutemouths & Trumpetfishes

Though it is relatively easy to approach these stick-like fishes, they are a pain to compose for pictures. Being of longish body, a frontal shot will land up with no nose room but plenty of headroom. Try positioning them diagonally or go for a close-up shot.

•llow phase

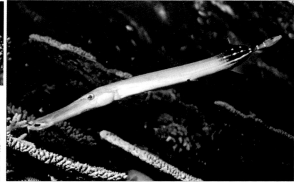

Trumpetfish
Aulostomus chinensis
80cm Indo-Pacific -common
GBR, Australia
60mm f11 1/125sec

Using a Coral cod
as shelter to
ambush prey.
Aulostomus chinensis
Kimbe Bay, PNG
60mm f8 1/125sec

Smooth flutemouth
Fistularia commersonii
*150*cm,mostly Indo-Pacific
Milne Bay, PNG
60mm f11, 1/60sec

Rockcods, Coral Trout, Groupers, Sea Basses, Basslets, Soapfishes and Podges are all common names given to members of this huge family. Due to the diversity within the family, in recent years some genera have been classified as sub-families of the Serranidae family tree.

Getting to Know ROCK-CODS (Sub family: *Epinephelinae)*

Groupers, Rockcods and Coral trouts are classified in the sub-family *Epinephelinae*. Despite their many different names their solid torpedo shaped body with prominent jaws, canine teeth, a continuous dorsal fin with obvious spiny section, mottled patterns and descriptive camouflage colours can easily identify the family.

Groupers are large fish and make up more than 150 species in over 20 genera. Some grow to at least 2 metres(6ft), weigh up to 200kg(440lb), and can live for more than 50 years. Other rockcod members are small to medium sized fish.

Domain of ROCK-CODS AND FAIRY BASSLETS

Rock-cods are reef dwellers living a solitary existence, usually with only one or two cod living on any part of the reef. Basslets live in specific habitats of corals or caves but can typically be found at drop-offs at the reef's edge at depths of up to 45m(150ft).

Eat or Be Eaten

All members of these families are carnivores equipped with several rows of sharp teeth. Additionally, fish-eating species are usually distinguished by their prominent canines at the front of the jaw. Feeding mainly on fish and crustaceans they are the top reef predators, usually lurking in the reef waiting to ambush their prey. Dining at dusk they use their large elastic mouths to create a suction to pull the prey in and then seize it with their teeth. Basslets are tasty prey for Moray Eels (Muraenidae) and Scorpionfish (Scorpaenidae) as well as for their bigger cousins, the Groupers.

Coral cod
Cephalopholis miniata
<u>40</u>cm, widespread
Tulamben, Bali
60mm f11 1/60sec

Sixspot rockcod
Cephalopholis sexmaculatus
<u>40</u>cm, Indo-Pacific
Kimbe Bay, PNG
60mm f11 1/125sec

Peacock rockcod
Cephalopholis argus
<u>40</u>cm, Indo-Pacific
Mergui, Myanmar
60mm f11 1/60sec

Spotted rockcod
Plectropomous maculatus
60cm, Indo-Australasia Arch.
Coral Sea, Australia
60mm f11 1/125sec

Rock Cods & Basslets Serranidae

In Bed with Rock Cods

Most groupers in the sub-family *Epinephelinae*, start life as females and, after one or more years of spawning, change into males. When it is time to procreate they gather in pairs, or in a group in the twilight at the outer edge of the reef. A brief courtship of exaggerated swimming by the male ensues before he ascends to the surface together with the female to release their eggs and sperm.

Spawning begins when the female, laden with eggs, approaches a prospective mate. She begins by swimming in an S-curve formation, with her fins fully erect, and then quivers in front of her male. If the mate is keen he will follow her in a slow jerky swimming pattern. The male nudges the female's distended belly at which point she blanches and the male develops a conspicuous barred pattern. The S-curving and jerk-swimming accelerate to a crescendo when the pair dash up from the bottom to shed their eggs and sperm.

Gifted with a bizarre variation of hermaphroditism, the Serranidae sub-family, found mainly in the Atlantic and East Pacific, have what we would perhaps call a great sex life; certainly a interesting one. The scientific term is "Simultaneous Hermaphroditism" meaning that each individual produces both eggs and sperm. Quite simply this means that when it comes to spawning both the female and male alternate their roles, one lays eggs while the other sheds sperm and then vice versa.

For this sub-family, after the first spawning the pair resumes the courtship with the partners reversing roles. The couple engaged in spawning will continue for several hours alternating the male and female roles.

left -
Barramundi cod
Cromileptes altivelis
60cm, West Pacific to
Nicobar Is.
Milne Bay, PNG
60mm f11 1/60sec

Potato cod
Epinephelus tukula
1.8m, West -Pacific
Cod Hole, Australia
15mm f 8 1/125sec

Footballer cod
Plectropomus laevis
100cm, Maldives to GBR
GBR, Australia
60mm f8 1/60sec

Malabar grouper
Epinephelus malabaricus
1.2m, Indian Ocean
Ari Atoll, Maldives
60mm f11 1/125sec

(Sub-family:Anthiinae)

Getting to Know Fairy BASSLETS

These pretty fish, sometimes referred to as the "fairies" of the reef, are typically seen in large congregations. They provide a plethora of colour to the reef, seen in groups flushed with shades of electric pink, yellow, violet, green, orange and magenta. Conspicuous by their abundance they form an important part of coral reef fauna.

If you see a group of brightly coloured small slender fish hovering above hard coral, an educated guess would be that they are fairy basslets. Other 'tell-tale' clues to look for are their forked caudal tail closely resembling a 'mermaids' tail. All of them sport a long continuous dorsal fin and long anal and pelvic fins, both filamentous and flimsy in texture. Reaching a maximum length of 15cm(7"), the males are usually more colourful than females and some of them have delicate extended third spines protruding from their dorsal fin or tail.

Basslets or Anthias belong to a family of 23 genera with nearly 100 species and are distributed in all tropical oceans, although they are especially abundant on the reefs of the Indo-Pacific. They are gregarious fish and can often be seen feeding on zooplankton, or foraging in large groups among coral outcrops or on the reef's edge during the day. At the first approach of danger however they quickly descend to shelter among corals or rocks, which also offer them protection whilst sleeping at night.

Pink anthias (male)
Pseudanthias hypselosoma
<u>12cm</u> Samoa to Maldives
Tulamben, Bali
105mm f16 1/60sec

Yellow fairy basslet
Pseudanthias evansi
<u>10</u>cm,East Africa to Maldives
Ari Atoll, Maldives
105mm f16 1/60sec

Indian flame basslet
Pseudanthias ignitus
<u>6</u>cm, endemic Maldives
Felidhoo, Maldives
105mm f16 1/125sec

Scalefin anthias
Pseudanthias squamipinnis
15cm, West Pacific to E.Africa
Bunaken, Nth Sulawesi
105mm f16 1/60sec

Rock Cods & Basslets

In Bed with Basslets

Basslets are also hermaphrodites. They start life as females and change to males in later life. The stimulus for the sex change has been attributed to size, age or the removal of the dominant male in a group. This removal results in the biggest female changing her colour pattern and sex to that of the dominant male predecessor and taking control over his group of sub-ordinate females. The complete physical switch is complete within a couple of days. Upon the dawning of the spawning season, small groups of females and males split off from the reef and regroup near their pre-selected mating sites on the outer reef. While some males may be territorial, others may not be. All males however erect their fins and quickly change into courtship colours. The time for their communion occurs after dusk, preceded by the male display of zig-zag swimming and dipping up and down. Spawning for the female basslet is a very brief affair involving no foreplay from her partner. If a female responds to the male 'strut' she approaches the male and they briefly come together for a few seconds when the eggs and sperm are instantly shed. Not having much time for such nonsense the female spawns only once a night and then returns to her activities, while the male continues to spawn with as many females as possible. Spawning by several pairs may take place simultaneously. Their pelagic eggs hatch in less than 24 hours.

Shooting Fairy Basslets & Rock Cods

There are the bold and there are the timid. Fishes of these families are both!
They are territorial hence it is best to photograph them in their territory. You will find them looking out at you from beneath coral tables or wrecks. A period of bonding is usually required to take pictures.

I have always enjoyed taking pictures of basslets. They are extremely colourful and a joy to watch. These dainty fishes almost seem to communicate with you. Quite often you will see one looking straight at you for a few seconds before dashing off in another direction. A 105mm lens is essential.

(female)

Squarespot anthias
Pseudanthias pleurotaenia
20cm Indo-Australasia Arch.
Bali, Indonesia
105mm f16 1/60sec

(male)

Red-stripe basslet
Pseudanthias fasciatus
15cm rare, deepwater Indo-Pacific
Siau, Nth Sulawesi
105mm f16 1/60sec

Purple anthias
Pseudanthias tuka
12cm, Indo Australasia Arch.
Coral Sea, Australia
105mm f22 1/60sec

Stocky anthias
Pseudanthias hypselosoma
19cm, Samoa to Maldives
Bunaken, Nth Sulawesi
105mm f16 1/125sec

Perhaps it is the gentle and sweet appearance of Haemulidae that earn it the common name of Sweetlips instead of its other more appropriate name of Gruntfish. Sweetlips emit rude grunting noises made by the grinding of their pharyngeal teeth and when their bladder further amplifies this sound, they are one of the noisiest inhabitants of the tropical coral reef.

Getting to Know SWEETLIPS

Sweetlips resemble the laterally compressed body shape of a Snapper (*Lutjanidae*) but they look much friendlier with a smaller mouth, smacking thick lips and no canine teeth. Predominantly the adult species are bright yellow with black stripes or spots. The juveniles vary dramatically from the adult, being either black and white in colour or sporting white spots with dark brown segments. One prime example is the juvenile *P. chaetodontoides,* commonly known as the Clown Sweetlips due to its resemblance to Anemonefish (*Amphiprion*) in shape and its clownish antics of swimming in a head down position on the reef bottom. When it matures to adulthood it changes shape to a lateral compressed body decorated with symmetrical brown spots on a faint yellow body. (See title page of this book).

Small to medium size fish they range in size from 10-50cm. (3" to 15") and come from a small family of only 120 species of 18 genera in the world ocean.

Oriental Sweetlips
Plectorhinchos orientalis
<u>86cm</u> E Africa to Samoa
Nth Male' Atoll, Maldives
105mm f16 1/60sec

Spotted sweetlips (juv)
<u>*Plectorhinchus sp.*</u>
<u>50</u>cm, West Pacific
Togian Islands, Sulawesi
60mm f11, 1/60sec

Diagonal banded sweetlips
<u>*Plectorhinchus lineatus*</u>
<u>50</u>cm, West Pacific
Tulamben, Bali
60mm f11, 1/60sec

Sweetlips Haemulidae

Domain of SWEETLIPS
Sweetlips are primarily nocturnal feeders. During the day they 'hangout' in pairs or in groups beneath coral plates or small caves.

Eat or Be Eaten
At dusk they separate from their group to forage the outer edge of the reef, vacuuming the sandy bottom with their rubbery lips, feeding on benthic invertebrates.

In Bed with Sweetlips
The mating behaviour of Sweetlips has never been conclusively recorded but it is thought to be similar to that of the Grouper (Serranidae) and snapper. It is assumed that they spawn in groups at night along the outer reef.

Shooting Sweetlips
Generally shy, when approached during the day Sweetlips will retire deeper into their hideouts. It is easier to get closer to them at dusk when they are actively feeding. Successful pictures can be captured with 35mm to 60mm lens.

Harlequin sweetlips - juv
Plectorhinchus chaetodonoides
60cm Maldives to Samoa
Nth Male Atoll, Maldives
60mm f11 1/60sec

juvenile

Harlequin sweetlips
Plectorhinchus chaetodonoides
<u>60cm</u> Maldives to Samoa
Nth Male Atoll, Maldives
24mm f8 1/60sec

Netted sweetlips
Plectorhinchus flavomaculatus
cm, E. Africa to West Pacific
Ningaloo Reef, Australia
60mm f11, 1/60sec

Yellow-ribbon sweetlips
<u>*Plectorhinchus polytaenia*</u>
<u>5</u>0cm, Indo-Australasia Arch.
Bunaken, Nth Sulawesi
60mm f11, 1/60sec

Getting to Know Snappers

Members of the Snapper family are in spite of their name, shy and timid fish. The Blue-Striped Snapper *(Lutjanus kasmira)* is one of the most prominent members of the 'snapping' family encountered on a coral reef. The Snapper or Seaperch can be distinguished by its elongated profile, semi-solid body, single dorsal fin and often visible canine teeth. Medium to large fish up to 2m(6 1/2ft) in length, they are typically 'fish' shaped in many different colours. The single most distinctive characteristic to look out for are their long pointed faces, giving their head the profile of an isosceles triangle. They live a relatively long lifespan of between 4-21 years. Over 100 species in 17 genera, they inhabit all tropical seas but the majority of species, including the blue-striped snapper, are found in the Indo-Pacific.

Domain of SNAPPERS

They inhabit shallow to intermediate reef depths up to 100m(330ft) and some deeper water species can be found in depths of 500m(1650 ft). Gregarious fish they tend to mill around in small to large congregations during the day. Though they roam over a great distance, they are never too far from the shelter of coral. At night the group breaks rank and they fan out on the reef in search of food.

Eat or Be Eaten

Active predators, snappers usually dine at night feeding on their staple diet of smaller fish supplemented by crabs, shrimps, crustaceans and planktonic organisms. Snappers are popular on the human dinner table but they take their revenge! They are often the cause of food poisoning as a result of harbouring a toxin called ciguatera in their skin. This is caused by their herbivorous diet of Surgeonfishes (Acanthuridae) and Parrotfishes (Scaridae) who eat and accumulate the causative microorganisms of algae or dead corals.

In Bed with Snappers

Snappers mate at night. Prior to spawning activities the in-shore species migrate in a group to the outer reef to select a spawning site. The group separates into smaller units consisting of males pursuing either one or more females. There is a brief pairing period where the male nuzzles the female's anal area before the groups gather and regroup to reach an orgasmic ascent. At the peak of their union, gametes and eggs are dispersed into the water column. Their pelagic eggs hatch within 24 hours. When the young are old enough to feed they forage for food individually during the day. When they reach about 80mm(3") they congregate together and forage at night, moving to deeper waters.

Shooting Snappers

Snappers never sit still unless you can briefly corner them for a picture. Watch them for a while in the area where they forage. The element of surprise is the secret.

Paddletail snapper
Lutjanus gibbus
50cm E Africa to GBR
Milne Bay, PNG
28mm f8 1/60sec

juvenile

Midnight snapper
Macolor macularis
*60*cm,East Indies to GBR
Layang Layang, Malaysia
60mm f11, 1/60sec

Blue-striped snapper
Lutjanus kasmira
*35*cm, E. Africa to Polynesia
Ari Atoll, Maldives
60mm f16 1/60sec

Yellow margined snapper
Lutjanus fulvus
40cm, Indo-Pacific
Kunak, Malaysia
60mm f11 1/60sec

The schools of small blue silvery fishes that are frequently seen around the coral reef realm are Fusiliers. Previously they were considered a sub-family of the Snapper family *(Lutjanidae)*, but with some serious contentions the new family of *Caesionidae* has now evolved as a family in its own right in the world of fishes.

Getting to Know FUSILIERS

Fusiliers are fast swimming schooling species, with a slender streamlined body and forked tailed. Closely related to snappers, they are generally small fishes but a few species reach up to 50cm(24"). They have highly protrusible jaws with a small mouth adapted for plucking plankton. Typically they are of an almost fluorescent bluish and yellow colour with lines or blotches that make them easily identifiable.

The Black-tip Fusilier *(Pterocaesio marri)* has black tips on either side of its forked tail while the Duo-tone Neon Fusilier *(Pterocaesio tile)* is easily identifiable by its split level half and half colouration of green and orange.

Domain of FUSILIERS

Being small in size, Fusiliers convene in schools for the added protection of safety in numbers. By schooling they also achieve greater energy efficiency from each other by the vacuum in the vortex created by the fish swimming in front. Should fusiliers sense any danger, a signal is sent through the school and it contracts into a gleaming blue mass to confuse the predator. A delinquent that ventures out of school will easily be taught a lesson at his peril.

Gold & Blue fusilier
Caesio xanthonota
22cm E Africa to Maldives
Maaya thila, Maldives
105mm f11 1/60sec

Marr's fusiler
Pterocaesio marri
30cm, East Africa to GBR
GBR, Australia
105mm f11 1/60sec

Goldstriped fusilier
Caesio caerulaurea
22cm, India to GBR
GBR, Australia
60mm f11 1/125sec

Goldstriped fusilier
Caesio caerulaurea
22cm, India to GBR
GBR, Australia
60mm f11 1/125sec

Actively roaming coastal and outer reefs in the day they love to hang in the current to feed on fast moving plankton, especially during tidal changes. At night they retire for sleep in the evening amongst the safety of the coral crevices. As a deterrent to potential predators, the Neon fusiliers turn on a red nightlight in their belly when they sleep. There are about 20 species in 4 genera of Fusiliers found in the Indo-Pacific tropical waters.

Eat or be Eaten
Fusiliers are plankton eaters, actively feeding in the water column by day; as such they are potential prey for pelagic fishes.

In Bed with FUSILIERS
Though juvenile fusiliers are almost indistinguishable from those of a snapper, it would not be wrong to assume that fusiliers participate in schooling sex while their Cousins the snappers enjoy spawning in small groups. Being a young family, there are not many references on their courtship or spawning behavior.

Shooting FUSILIERS
Hang out on the edge of coral reefs and wait for them to swim past. Remember they are fast swimmers and silvery hence your selection of film and exposure has to be 'spot on'. Generally I would use Fuji Professional D 100 ASA film and a 24mm or 60mm lens.

Neon fusilier - day
Pterocaesio tile
22cm E Africa to Fiji
Sipadan, Malaysia
60mm f11 1/60sec

Neon fusilier - night
Pterocaesio tile
22cm E Africa to Fiji
Bunaken, Nth Sulawesi
60mm f16 1/60sec

Red bellied fusilier - day
Caesio cuning
25cm, Indo-Pacific
Maldives
60mm f11 1/60sec

Red-bellied fusilier - night
Caesio cuning
25cm, Indo-Pacific
GBR, Australia
60mm f11 1/60sec

Getting to Know Jacks

Jacks or trevallies predominantly inhabit outer reef slopes. They are mid-water to surface fishes that hunt in small packs of four or five to schools of thousands. They are diurnal fishes that have a strong presence on the reef where they thrive. They are early risers, seen active from dawn to dusk. Jacks are active throughout the day and species such as the Bluefin Trevally will every so often terrorize reef fishes in an electrifying melee. The Carangidae family is a sleek, silvery, streamlined shape with a laterally compressed body. Characteristics include prominent deeply forked caudal fin (tail) and a slender tail base. Most species have posterior scales laterally lined resembling spiny, plate-like structures, called scutes. Sizes of jacks vary, ranging from about 20cm for the Smooth-tailed Yellow-lined Trevally (Selaroides leptolepis) to the Giant Trevally (Caranx ignobilis), which grows to a respectable 180cm.

Domain of Jacks

Jacks mainly inhabit tropical waters, with widespread distribution for quite a few species. Currently, they are classified into 25 genera, with a species diversity of about 140. Whilst they are not strictly reef fishes, they are commonly found on reef edges and outer reef walls. Though some schools are known to roam for great distances, many resident schools have been observed in Bali, Maldives and Malaysia. Particularly, two large schools of over a 1000 have been predictably found in Tulamben Bay, North West Bali since 1995. The most common species found on the Australian Great Barrier Reef and in Indonesia are the Bluefin Trevally (Caranx melampygus). Though some species such as the Golden Trevally feed largely on crustaceans and molluscs, most are voracious predators that feed on a variety of fishes.

In Bed with Jacks

Courtship and mating among jacks is best observed later in the afternoon in deep water channels or outer reef slopes. Where they congregate, males may be seen actively pursuing running females in heat. Eventually, they pair up, with the male donning a dark courtship colour, signaling that he is the successful male. He will swim with the female in a tight circle, as if in her shadow from the water column to reef bottom. Gametes and eggs are shed in huge numbers at the height of the communion. After 24 hours in the pelagic zone, the eggs hatch to produce large headed larvae with prominent eyes and jaws. By the time they grow to about 8-9mm, they are easily recognized as small jacks. While some juveniles inhabit the relative safe haven of lagoons and inshore waters, some juvenile species are seen gallivanting the vast oceans, under the protection of mantas, jellyfish and whale sharks.

Shooting Jacks

Jacks are not easily spooked. If approached cautiously, it is possible to swim among them. Both wide angle and portraits of jacks are easily attained. When using strobes, the element of their reflective body often causes images to be over exposed.

Bigeye trevally
Caranx sexfasciatus
<u>70cm</u> Indo-Pacific
Maldives
60mm f11 1/60sec

Bluefin trevally
Caranx melampygus
<u>100cm</u> Indo-Pacific to the Americas
GBR, Australia
28mm f11 1/60sec

Goldbody trevally
Carangoides bajad
<u>50</u>cm, Indo-Pacific Arch.
New Britain, PNG
60mm f8 1/125sec

Black trevally
Caranx lugubris
80cm, Indo-Australasia Arch.
Layang Layang, Malaysia
35mm f8 1/60sec

Batfishes Ephippidae

Getting to Know BATFISHES

Batfishes are often sighted hanging motionlessly among coral outcrops or coral trees. They belong to the Ephippidae family, which is renown for their extravagant finnage. The juveniles in particular, being completely different in appearance to the adults, are conspicuous by their exotic, long, flowing, bat-like fins.

A graceful fish, Batfishes or Spadefishes are easy to recognize with their flattened appearance, circular body and elongated symmetrical dorsal and anal fins. Already of distinctive appearance, some species even have elongated pelvic fins. They are medium sized fish reaching a maximum length of 65cm(1 1/2ft). The family consists of about 17 species in 5 genera.

The transformation from juveniles to adults is dramatic. Adults are shades of brown black and silver with thick stripes or vertical bands across the eye, body and posterior part of the body. Juveniles are darker in colour and often have a thin orange or red colour bordering their fins. Juveniles also have exaggerated long dorsal and anal fins that decrease in length as they approach adulthood. The juvenile Teira Tall-fin Batfish (Platax teira) pictured opposite has almost completely assumed adult colours but still has the orange rim bordering its fins to show that it has not quite reached maturity.

Domain of BATFISHES

They are usually seen swimming in schools in relatively shallow waters (up to 20m/70ft) in both sheltered in-shore reefs and along offshore drop-offs further out. Some species can be found in deeper waters to depths of over 40m(140ft). They are commonly found on all tropical reefs in the Indo-Pacific and some of the most graceful species are from the genus Platax. Hanging out in schools or in small groups amongst coral trees during the day they retire into crevices and ledges for protection at night. Batfishes can be extremely friendly and curious and it is not uncommon to be surrounded by a group of the nosey fish.

Hump-headed batfish
Platax batavianus
<u>50cm</u> Indo-Australasia Arch.
Bunaken, Nth Sulawesi
60mm f11 1/60sec

Teira batfish (juv)
Platax teira
<u>50</u>cm, Indo-Pacific
Tulamben, Bali
60mm f11, 1/125sec

Teira batfish
Platax teira
<u>50</u>cm, Indo-Pacific
Maldives
60mm f16, 1/125sec

Batfishes Ephippidae

Juvenile Antics

Some juveniles, such as those of the leafy coloured Orbicular Batfish (*Platax orbicularis*), are masters of disguise using mimicry to protect themselves against predators. By pretending to play dead on the surface, lying on their side mimicking dead leaves, the hunted become the hunters. As they drift unnoticed on the surface amongst shoals of fry fish, they seize an easy dinner swimming alongside.

Eat or Be Eaten

The Teira Tall-fin Batfish (*Platax tiera)* is particularly tame and some species can even be handled. Their staple diet consists of benthic invertebrates and zooplankton, and it is not uncommon to find them in a school hanging and feeding in the current.

In Bed with BATFISHES

Not much is known about their reproductive habits but it is thought that their courtship and spawning activities are similar to the Angelfish *(Pomacanthidae)*. Spawning in pairs they slowly spiral to the surface to shed gametes and eggs. Hatching occurs within 24 hours (at a water temperature of 27C) and the larvae remains in the planktonic layer until they are about 10mm (5/8") before settling onto the reef.

Shooting BATFISHES

The Platax batfishes are the curious ones and they often circle divers. This makes them an easy target for the camera. Batfishes make good underwater pictures. The best profiles are from an upward angle, which exaggerates their features. A 20mm lens is required for a group atmospheric shot while a 60mm is recommended for portraits.

Short-finned batfish
Zabidius novemaculeatus
<u>40cm</u> Northern Australia
Lady Elliot, GBR
15mm f8 1/60sec

Pinnate batfish (juv)
Platax pinnatus
<u>30</u>cm, Indo-Australasia Arch.
Derawan, Indonesia
60mm f11, 1/60sec

Pinnate batfish
adolescent to adult stage
Platax pinnatus
<u>30</u>cm, Indo-Pacific
Ningaloo Reef, Australia
60mm f16, 1/60sec

Getting to Know BUTTERFLYFISHES

Reaching a maximum length of 30cm(12") this conspicuous group of reef fishes has distinctive colour patterns. Many species have a false 'eyespot' near the tail or below the dorsal fin with a stripe or solid black bar across their real eye, presumably to help confuse predators. Along with the stripes across the body, bright yellow is the colour that features frequently in this family. Colour patterns aside, they are easy to recognize by their physical appearance; a compressed flat disc shape, a continuous often heavily scaled dorsal fin, and in some cases a prominent elongated snout, like that of the Longnose Butterflyfish (*Forciper longirostris*).

Domain of BUTTERFLYFISHES

There are 120 species and 10 genera to this family, also called Coral fishes and Bannerfishes. They are found in tropical, sub-tropical and warm temperate waters. The majority of Butterflyfishes are located in the Indo-Pacific. Most species can be found in depths of less than 20m(44ft) though you may find some species at depths in excess of 200m(660ft).

Butterflyfishes are seen in abundance on the reef, staying close to the reef surface during the day feeding on coral polyps and zooplankton. Pyramid Butterflyfish (*Hemitaurichthys polylepis)* can be found in groups of over 200 traversing the seas of North Sulawesi. At night they seek shelter close to the reefs surface nestling in coral crevices and sponges. Being well protected, they can afford to shut down their colours for the night.

Apart from the Chevron Butterflyfish (*Chaetodon trifascialis*), most butterflyfishes are easy-going placid characters, neither territorial nor aggressive. With few enemies they are often 'just there' swimming in the background. Butterflyfish society, like that of most reef fishes, is composed of a range of social units, from foraging schools to solitary home lovers. For most species, the typical social unit is a heterosexual pair that remains permanent partners.

Spot-tail butterflyfish
Chaetodon ocellicaudus
14cm Indo-Australasia Arch.
GBR, Australia
60mm f11 1/125sec

Beaked Coralfish
Chelmon rostratus
20cm, Indo-Pacific
Ari Atoll, Maldives
60mm f11, 1/125sec

night 'gown' - colour is
toned down to sleep.

Latticed butterflyfish
C*haetodon rafflesi*
5cm,mostly South East Asia
Bunaken, Nth Sulawesi
60mm f11, 1/60sec

Butterflyfishes Chaetodontidae

Eat or Be Eaten

Size and shape of the jaws differ widely to meet different dietary requirements. Many species have short jaws to nip off live coral polyps, such as the Ornate Butterflyfish (*Chaetodon ornatissimus*) of which coral polyps are its staple diet. Others like the longnose butterflyfish have elongated jaws used to pick small invertebrates from among sea urchin spines and coral crevices. A few species feed in midwater on zooplankton whilst others have a mixed diet of small invertebrates and algae. The name '*Chaetodont*' refers to the bristle like teeth possessed by all members of family.

In Bed with Butterflyfishes

Generally spawning takes place at dusk and is initiated by the male after selecting his spawning territory. He courts the female by swimming just in front of her fluttering his body. When she signals that she is ready by ascending in the water a little, the male swims around her nudging her abdomen with his snout, whilst they both slowly ascend to the surface. Sperm and eggs are released high up in the water column, hatching in about 30 hours. Unique to butterflyfishes is the prolonged larval stage, where the larvae may remain in the planktonic layer for 2-3 months before settling to the bottom as juveniles.

Shooting Butterflyfishes

Though slow swimmers you can quickly become exhausted when chasing after a pair of butterflyfishes. Start by observing them from a distance. They usually follow a set path, weaving and feeding blithesomely among corals swimming in one direction. Position yourself ahead of them and wait for them to approach and in most cases you will have a chance to fire off a few frames before they are spooked away. Though it is easier to photograph them at night, they will have shut down their colors and pictures will look dull and uninteresting.

Bennet's butterflyfish
Chaetodon bennetti
_8cm_ E. Africa to Pitcairn Is,
South Male, Maldives
60mm f11 1/125sec

Pyramid butterflyfish
Hemitaurichthys polylepis
_18_cm, Indo-Pacific
Sipadan, Malaysia
60mm f11, 1/60sec

Pacific double-saddle
butterflyfish
Chaetodon ulietensis
_15_cm, Indo-Australasia Arch.
GBR, Australia
60mm f11, 1/125sec

Eye-patch butterflyfish
Chaetodon adiergastos
_18cm_ West Australia to Java
Layang Layang, Malaysia
60mm f11 1/69sec

Longnose butterflyfish
Forcipiger longirostris
_20_cm Indo-Pacific
Komodo, Indonesia
60mm f16, 1/60sec

Yellowhead butterflyfish
C_haetodon xanthocephalus_
_18_cm,Indian Ocean
Nth Male Atoll, Maldives
60mm f11, 1/60sec

Rainford's butterflyfish
Chaetodon rainfordi
15cm Great Barrier Reef
Heron Island, GBR, Australia
60mm f11 1/125sec

Longfin bannerfish
Heniochus acuminatus
*25*cm, Indo-Pacific
Kimbe Bay, PNG
28mm f11, 1/60sec

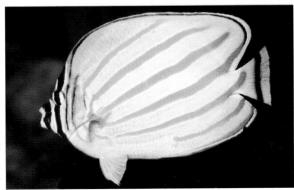

Ornate butterflyfish
Chaetodon ornatissimus
*20*cm,Indo-Pacific.
GBR, Australia
60mm f11, 1/125sec

Getting to Know ANGELFISHES

Angelfishes are regarded as some of the most beautiful of all reef fishes with their brilliant colours and patterns. They have been bestowed species titles of Emperor, Regal, Queen and King Angelfish, which speak for themselves. Crowning the Neptunian reef with their ethereal presence they can hardly fail to attract the attention of any audience.

Close relatives of Butterflyfish (*Chaetodontidae*), they bear a strong resemblance in appearance sharing the compressed flat disc shape, single long continuous dorsal and anal fins, and small mouth with bristle-like teeth.

An Angelfish, however, can be fairly easily distinguished from its first cousin. Still a small to medium sized fish, from 7-46cm(3-15"), they tend to be larger, more brightly and luminously coloured, and have more pronounced and rough-edged scales than the Butterflyfish. Look out for the strong long spine at the corner of the preopercle, near the pectoral fin that is absent on Butterflyfish.

Angelfish males are larger than females in most genera and colour differences exist between the sexes. Details vary from one species to another but generally males have stripes, they are brightly coloured and have pronounced caudal fins. Females are more drably coloured, lack stripes and have dark upper and lower margins on the caudal fin. Colour patterns also differ between juveniles and adults.

Domain of ANGELFISHES

Approximately 80 species in 9 genera can be found in tropical and sub-tropical reefs. Many species inhabit shallow waters from a one metre(3ft) to 15m(50ft). Others are restricted to deeper waters in depths of up to 75m(200ft).

Angelfishes are dependent on the presence of shelter in the form of boulders, caves and coral crevices. Typically territorial, they spend the daylight hours near the bottom searching for food, retiring to their crevices at night. Living alone, in pairs or small groups they are shy creatures keeping their distance from divers and snorkellers. Often out of sight sheltering in a large coral head, the larger species can produce a series of loud low-frequency recognizable drumming sounds that can surprise the unwary diver.

juvenile

Emperor angelfish
Pomacanthus imperator
<u>38cm</u> Indo-Pacific
GBR, Australia
60mm f11 1/60sec

Three-spot angelfish
A*polemichthys trimaculatus*
<u>25cm</u> E Afirca to Samoa
Maldives
60mm f16 1/60sec

Six-banded angelfish
Pomacanthus sexstriatus
<u>22</u>cm, Malaysia to Solomon Is
Aur, Malaysia
60mm f11 1/125sec

Regal angelfish
Pygoplites diacanthus
<u>26cm</u>, Indo-Pacific
Bunaken, Nth Sulawesi
60mm f11 1/60sec

Eat or Be Eaten

Diet varies with species, from those that feed exclusively on algae or sponges supplemented by a mélange of benthic invertebrates, to those that are midwater Plankton feeders.

In Bed with Angelfishes

The Angelfishes' social unit varies, from couples to a male-dominated harem comprised of a small number of females. Like some other families Angelfishes usually have sex reversal capabilities clearly demonstrated in their harem society. In this instance should the male disappear the largest dominant female will change sex and take on her old partners role, assuming that in her Bodicea fashion she successfully defeats the attempted coups of other neighbouring males. Within a few days she can be behaving as a male and within 3 weeks the sex reversal is complete.

Spawning activity varies from genus to genus but generally occurs at dusk involving a single pair of fish. Sessions are preceded by the male establishing a temporary spawning territory, typically around a prominent coral outcrop along the reef. Territorial disputes between males may ensue over the best sites but once these have been settled the male ascends and awaits the arrival of the female. On her approach he will swim above her in full courtship display with all fins extended.

If the female is suitably impressed she ascends to join him. The pair then slowly spiral towards the surface with the male swimming around his mate and nuzzling her abdomen to heighten her arousal. Once near the surface, in a sudden orgasmic burst hundreds of gametes of eggs and sperm are released simultaneously. Their encounter quickly over, the female heads back to the reef whilst the male continues to 'sow his oats' as long as there are willing females present, repeatedly spawning with many females that evening if he is lucky. Hatching occurs within 24 hours and the juveniles settle to the bottom when they are about three to four weeks old.

Shooting Angelfishes

The royals are not really keen to grant an audience to the marine photographer. Their presence requires a royal salute of patience and dedication. Learn to catch them while they are on the move among coral heads and overhangs. Effective strobe positioning is essential for a good portrait shot. Expose your film about 1/2-1 stop under, to bring out their royal colours

Lamarck's angelfish
Genicanthus lamarck
<u>20cm</u> common in PNG Indo-Pacific
Milne Bay, PNG
60mm f11 1/60sec

Bi-color angelfish
Centropyge bicolor
<u>15cm</u> Indo Australasia Arch.
Togians , Central Sulawesi
60mm f11 1/60sec

Pearl-scaled angelfish
Centropyge vrolikii
<u>10</u>cm, Indian Ocean to Micronesia
Kimbe Bay, PNG
105mm f11 1/160sec

juvenile

Semi-circle angelfish
Pomacanthus semicirculatus
<u>38cm</u>, Maldives to W. Australia
Ningaloo, W Australia
60mm f11 1/60sec

Getting to Know DAMSELFISHES

The family of Damselfish is easily one of the most prolific and common groups of fish that you are likely to encounter on a reef. Darting in and out among corals, sponges, anemones and gorgonian fans there are over 320 species worldwide. A feature of this family apart from its size is diversity of habitat, diet, behaviour and colouration.

Their popular ambassador to the world is of course the famous Clown or Anemonefish, which has a separate dedication in this book. These small fish range in size from a few centimeters to 30cm. They vary immensely in colour from fluorescent blues and yellows to drab hues of grey and black. Bearing resemblance to the shape of an arrowhead these hardy small characters can live up to the ripe old age of 10 years. Apart from shape and size other clues for identification include one continuous dorsal fin, a pronounced pelvic fin used for swimming, and moderately large scales. The caudal fin varies from fork to triangular.

Domain of DAMSELFISHES

While some Damselfishes, especially the Reticulated Dascyllus (*Dascyllus reticulatus*) and Blue Green Chromis *(Chromis viridis)* are found among hard coral, others use the entire reef as their playground and anemonefishes (*Amphripron sp.*) live exclusively with the sea anemone. Most species are found in shallow waters although some inhabit depths of up to 240 ft. (80m) (Dr G. Allen).

Active during the day they can be seen in groups or in pairs darting in out of their habitat. At night they take refuge amongst the protection of coral or in holes and crevices. Most Damselfishes are territorial, especially the algae eaters, defending their territory vigorously, charging at intruders regardless of their size. For the diver this can mean the occasional nip or pinch but it is nothing more than an annoyance, rarely penetrating the skin.

Princess Damsel
Pomacentrus vaiuli
10cm mainly West Pacific to Samoa
GBR, Australia
105mm f11 1/60sec

Blue devil
Chrysiptera cyanea
8cm Indo Australasia Arch. to Micronesia
Milne Bay, PNG
105mm f11 1/60sec

Bar cheek damselfish
Neoglyphidodon thoracotaeniatus
7cm, deepwater Indonesia
Togian, Central Sulawesi
105mm f11 1/60sec

Reticulated damsel
Dascyllus reticulatus
9cm, Indo-Australasia to Samoa
GBR, Australia
105mm f16 1/60sec

Eat or Be Eaten

The Damselfish diet ranges from a variety of invertebrates and algae to zooplankton. Studies have shown that there is a correlation between staple diet and behaviour. The vegetarian algae eaters tend to be much more aggressive and territorial and generally more drably coloured, whereas many of the zooplankton feeders are more brightly coloured, timid and belong to members of the family found in larger groups.

In Bed with Damselfishes

Damselfishes spawn sporadically, in the early morning, throughout the year peaking in the summer months. For those who do not have a permanent residence (the non-territorial zooplankton eaters), pre-spawning activity includes setting up a temporary territory before courtship. In this instance the adult male selects the spawning site and prepares the nest by digging out the sand and removing algae and shells.

During this preparation period the male becomes increasingly territorial and starts courting passing females by swimming directly in front of each one in an exaggerated fashion. He then abruptly turns around in the hope of leading her back to his love nest. To seduce his mating companions, the male dons a temporary exaggerated colour pattern during the mating game. The love dance is a complex one employing the use of colour, exaggerated movements and chirping sounds.

When a female is won over, she releases about 100 to 1000 eggs in the nest. The male circles her fiercely to defend them from other males. When she has finished he then quickly swims over and fertilizes them and assumes a single parent role of guarding and aerating the eggs until they hatch. The male may spawn with many females sequentially at the same nest site amassing thousands of eggs. Eggs are hatched within 2-7 days and the larvae rise to the surface to be transported by ocean currents for periods, specie dependent, between 10-50 days. Eventually the young fish settle on the bottom assuming the bright colours of juvenile colouration. They grow between 5-15mm per month. When they reach 25-30mm in length they leave the parents to form loose aggregations with the youngsters of other broods and adopt the slightly duller colours of adulthood. **Damselfish, Blennies, Gobies and Triggerfish are the few fish families that lay demersal eggs in a nest and practice parental care.**

Shooting Damselfishes

If your selected model is not in an agitated mood then she is mostly likely to test you to the limit by darting among the coral. The only way to catch her is by predicting her movement. Pre-focus your camera and like working with a super model, fire on every move. Again the right lens is essential, generally the 105mm macro.

Golden Damsel
Amblyglyphidodon aureus
12cm E Indian to W Pacific
GBR, Australia
60mm f11 1/60sec

Indo-Pacific sergeant
Abudefduf vaigiensis
*18*cm, Indo-Pacific
Tulamben, Indonesia
60mm f11 1/60sec

Three-spot dascyllus
Dascyllus trimaculatus
3cm, common, Indo-Australasia
GBR, Australia
60mm f16 1/60sec

Getting to Know WRASSES

The Wrasses are a huge family easily conspicuous by their variety and sheer abundance on the coral reef. One of their distinct and unique characteristics is the bird-like swimming action, flapping their pectoral fins just like the wings of a bird in flight.

Wrasses come in an array of shapes and sizes and vary in length from a few centimetres (Cleaner Wrasses) to the huge 2.3m (7ft) Napoleon Wrasse (*Cheilinus undulatus*). Their diversity is like a kaleidoscope with the most complex variation of colour patterns, forms and relationships. With such variation, their distinctive common external features are the unique beating of 'wings' style of swimming and the continuous dorsal fins. Other features to look out for in some common species are their thick lips and prominent canine teeth (buck-tooth appearance). Most wrasses are predominantly brightly coloured of composite pattern. An individualistic group, colours again vary between the gender and juveniles of each species. Within a group the dominant male is usually the most luminescent.

Domain of WRASSES

During the day wrasses are found swimming on every coral reef habitat alone, or in pairs or groups. A firm believer of early to bed but late to rise, wrasses retire into holes and crevices early in the evening and they are among the last to get up in the morning. Some of the smaller species sleep in a sand burrow. Happy to mind their own business they are timid creatures, non-territorial, and will tend to swim away from an approaching diver or snorkeller.

Eat or Be Eaten

All members of the wrasse family are carnivorous. With their powerful teeth and jaws they feed on an extensive menu of worms, crustaceans, small molluscs, sea urchins and chewing off coral polyps. Whilst some prefer to participate in eating frenzies feeding on zooplankton, others like the cleaner wrasses (e.g. *Labroides dimidiatus*) earn their meals by plucking off and eating parasites and algae living on the bodies of other species of fishes. There are also the sand sorting machines who ingest mouthfuls of sand, select the tiny animals and then rejecting the rest of the pile.

Slingjaw wrasse
Epibulus insidiator
<u>35cm</u> *Indo-* Pacific
GBR, Australia
60mm f11 1/60sec

Redbreasted maori wrasse
Cheilinus fasciatus
<u>36</u>cm, Micronesia to E Africa
Milne Bay, PNG
60mm f11 1/125sec

Chiseltooth wrasse
Pseudodax moluccanus
<u>25mm,</u> Indo-Pacific
Maldives
60mm f11 1/60sec

In Bed with Wrasses

Although traditionally of the two genders, sexuality is a complex issue in the society of Wrasses. Sex reversal is promminent, but unlike the damselfish it is the female who changes sex. In most species there are 2 types of male, those who are born male and stay that way, and those who start life as a female and in later life transform into functional males (changing to a much brighter colouration in the process). The stimulus for the sex change has been given as the correlation between males and social dominance, or less specifically simply a size-related factor (Thresher 1980). The cleaner wrasse *(Labroides dimidiatus)* is a prime example of the male/social dominance factor where a large male dominates a harem of up to 6 females. This harem is in itself composed of a strict hierarchy with the largest female holding the highest rank of principal concubine. This role affords her enormous power over the rest of the concubines, the only one being able to cohabit the males territory whilst being responsible for dominating the lower ranks of concubines. If the largest or any one of the females is removed, each concubines advances one position up the social ladder. If the male is removed, the largest female involves herself in a power struggle against neighbouring males who will attempt to take control of the territory and harem. If the female is large and aggressive enough to resist such coups, within a few hours she begins to assume the role and behaviour of a male and completes the physical change within a few days. Spawning occurs throughout the year on the edge or outer slope of a reef. Within this large family, and even within each species, spawning occurs in groups and in pairs. For those wrasses that spawn in a group, the group size may consist of a few to hundreds of fish. Spawning activity will commence with the fish slowly milling together to form a group. As the size of the group increases they swim faster and faster and more erratically, tightening up to form a very close-knit ball. At the height of the frenzy the whole group ascends into the water column then abruptly reverses direction leaving a mass of eggs and sperm behind which is soon dispersed into the current. With the pair spawning wrasse, the male sets up a temporary spawning territory on a prominent piece of coral or rock. From here he courts passing females, looping up and down in the water column and vibrating his body whilst swimming back and forth over a prospective mate. When she is ready the female signals to the courting male by arching her body in a 'S' shape proudly displaying her egg-laden belly. They then spawn in a rapid up and down dash to the surface. Spawning only takes place during a brief period each day depending on the local conditions. In areas with strong tidal currents spawning occurs just after peak high tide, ideal for transporting eggs off reef. Incubation varies with the water temperature - as an indication the eggs hatch just over 24 hours at 27C.

Shooting Wrasses

You must have the right lens for the job. 105mm, 60mm, to 24mm lenses are generally used. Unless you like fish tails, do not try to out swim even an unassuming slow moving wrasse. Ascend a few meters off the reef bottom and observe their feeding ground. Select a site and wait, and in most instances they will return to pick on morsels.

young adult

Napoleon wrasse
Cheilinus undulatus
largest recorded 2.29m
Indo-Pacific
Maldives
24mm f11 1/60sec

Blunthead wrasse
Thalassoma amblycephalum
15cm, Indo-Pacific
Bunaken, Nth Sulawesi
105mm f8 1/60sec

Harlequin Tuskfish
Choerodon fasciatus
30cm, GBR to New Caledonia
Heron Is. GBR, Australia
60mm f16 1/60sec

Golden wrasse
Halichoeres chrysus
12cm Western Pacific to East Indian
Tulamben, Bali
105mm f11 1/60sec

Bluehead fairy wrasse
Cirrhilabrus cyanopleura
1cm Indo Australasia Arch
Lembeh Strait, Nth Sulawesi
105m f11 1/125sec

Checkerboard wrasse
Halichoeres hortulanus
*26*cm, Indo-Pacific
Bunaken, Nth Sulawesi
50mm f11 1/60sec

Sneaky wrasse
Pteragogus sp.
15cm, Indo-Pacific
Maldives
60mm f11 1/125sec

Two-spot splendour wrasse
Cheilinus bimaculatus
15cm Indian Ocean
Bali, Indonesia
105mm f11 1/125sec

Splitlevel hogfish
Bodianus mesothorax
20m West Pacific to Fiji
Halmerhera, Indonesia
60mm f11 1/125sec

Yellowmoon wrasse
Thalassoma lutescens
24cm, Eastern Pacific
Kwajalein, Marshall Is.
60mm f11 1/60sec

juvenile

Rockmover wrasse
Novaculichthys taeniourus
30cm, Indo-Pacific
GBR, Australia
60mm f11 1/60sec

Getting to Know PARROTFISHES

The coral reef equivalent of the terrestrial Parrot is the *Scaridae* family, commonly known as Parrotfish. They are just as brightly coloured and are equipped with beak-like jaws of fused teeth similar to their terra firma equivalent. It is their mandible their and eating habits that makes them a major contributor of sediment to beaches and coral reefs.

With over 60 recognised species, parrotfishes look very similar to wrasses in body shape and colour pattern. They are distinguished, however, by their heavy body and beak with fused teeth. A medium to large fish, they reach up to 2m(6ft) in length Bumphead Parrot fish, (*Bolbometopon muricatum*) with varying colour patterns. These range from drab browns and blacks (typically juveniles and females) to complex and brilliant combinations of red green and blue of the larger males. Like their close relatives, Wrasses (*Labridae*), Parrotfishes have a continuous dorsal fin, relatively large scales and swim in the same bird-like fashion, flapping their pectoral fins.

Domain of PARROTFISHES.

Parrotfishes are typically seen browsing in groups of varying size across the coral reef. They also roam individually and the juveniles of some species live a solitary and secret existence. Active during the day, at night they sleep in small caves, beneath ledges and in rocks. Some species protect themselves by building a mucous cocoon around them at night. It takes them about 30 minutes to form the transparent sac and just about as long in the morning to discard it. The Parrotfish society is composed of nomadic species that wander in large foraging groups around a consistent part of the reef in a single area each day, and those that establish permanent territories on the reef. The wanderers are generally passive, more so than the permanent residents who are territorial in comparison. Having an established home to protect, each territory has one single male and one large dominant female with several sub-ordinate females. (See Wrasse Family, *Labridae*)

Ember parrotfish
Scarus rubroviolaceus
70cm Indo-Pacific
Tulamben, Indonesia
60mm f11 1/60sec

Bumphead parrotfish
Bolbometopon muricatum
*1.5*m, Indo-Pacific
Layang Layang, Malaysia
24mm f8 1/60sec

Indian Steephead Parrotfish
Scarus strongylocephalus
70cm, Indian Ocean
Maldives
60mm f11, 1/60sec

Eat or Be Eaten

Parrotfishes are herbivores using their strong beak jaws to scrape algae off dead corals and rocks. Some species feed on live coral. They not only consume vast quantities of algae but in the process pick up pieces of accompanying rock and coral to be pulverized in their jaws. To make their meal digestible, they further grind the algae and rocks to sand, before filtering through the goodies and returning the leftover sediment to the reef.

In Bed with Parrotfishes

Refer to Wrasse Family, *Labridae*

Shooting Parrotfishes

Parrotfishes make beautiful models. Up close at night their colours stand forth as if they have put on stage make-up for a theatrical performance. Locate them during night diving in crevices and you can be assured of a brilliant portrait. In the day, catch them if you can!

First time ever observed; Coral cod
sharing same cocoon with parrotfish
Rest Off Is., PNG
60mm f16, 1/60sec

Bluebarred parrotfish
Scarus ghobban
_75cm_ Indo-Pacific
Tulamben, Bali
60mm f11 1/125sec

Juvenile

Bi-color parrotfish
Cetoscarus bicolor
_80_cm, Indo-Pacific
GBR, Australia
60mm f11 1/60sec

Juvenile

Steephead Parrotfish
Scarus microrhinos
_70cm_, West Pacific & Oceania
Togian Island
60mm f11, 1/125sec

Getting to Know SURGEONFISHES

Surgeonfish are the gregarious and gentle but intrepid inhabitants of the coral reef. With distinctive features, they are characterized by the presence of a razor sharp spine on both sides of the caudal peduncle (base section of the tail area). Referred to as the 'scalpel' it is this spine, which gives the family its common surgical name. Surgeonfishes carry a retractable spine or spines on their caudal peduncle that may not be noticeable at a first glance. Surgeonfish can be identified by their flat typically oval, sometimes circular side profile enhanced by the continuous even dorsal and anal fins. Drab or brightly coloured they are medium to large sized solid fish ranging from 20-100cm(8-45"). Their small eyes are positioned high on their rounded head and they have conspicuous small mouths with incisor-like teeth suited to nibbling or scraping algae and plants from rocks or corals.

The 72 species of this family have been classified into 3 subfamilies; *Alcanthurinae, Nasinae, and Prionurinae*. The *Acanthurinae* is the largest sub-family with 36 species of which the Striped Surgeonfish (*Arcanthurus lineatus*) has a single venomous spine at the base of the tail area. Another sub-family Nasinae, or Unicornfish are equipped with one or two hook-like spines on either side of the tail base and they are easily distinguishable by the hump or unicorn horn protruding from their forehead. The females of some species have a much smaller horn, if any. Prionurinae are the rarer species and they are the ones with multiple bony tail plates.

Domain of SURGEONFISHES

Mostly found in the tropical waters of Indo-Pacific reefs in small groups or in shoals, they are typically seen in the day swimming in shallow water from 2m, though some species can be found transversing the depths of 100m(330ft). At night they sleep alone in coral crevices. Generally unassuming and timid, swimming away on your approach, they only use the spiny scalpel in defense against predators, and as an offensive weapon when engaged in combat with other fish. With a quick sweep of their tail, they are capable of fatally slashing other fish or causing serious lacerations to humans who manhandle them. In combat the fish warily circle their enemy with their spine angled towards them.

Orangeband surgeonfish
Acanthurus olivaceus
<u>35cm</u> Oceania to West Pacific
Bali, Indonesia
60mm f16 1/60sec

Powderblue surgeonfish
Acanthurus leucosternon
<u>22m</u> Indian ocean
Ari Atoll, Maldives
60mm f11 1/60sec

White-nose surgeonfish
Acanthurus japonicus
<u>15</u>cm, Indonesia to Japan
Layang Layang, Malaysia
60mm f11 1/125sec

Palette surgeonfish
Paracanthurus hepatus
<u>30cm</u>, E. Africa to Samoa
GBR, Australia
60mm f11 1/60sec

Surgeonfishes Acanthuridae

Eat or Be Eaten

Most fishes are typically predators; Surgeonfishes are one of the exceptions to the trait. They are mainly herbivores that graze on the plentiful supplies of algae on the reef. Some Surgeonfish have especially adapted digestive tracts that allow them to ingest sand whilst feeding, extracting the nutrients, and then excreting the waste. Scraping rocks or the coral surface also provides a varied diet. Unicornfish are an exception to their 'vegetarian' equivalents typically feeding in large aggregates on zoo-plankton.

In Bed with SURGEONFISHES

Surgeonfish courting and spawning activities are similar to many of their free-swimming counterparts, where pelagic eggs are typically produced in the water column after a short spawning ascent. Spawning typically takes place at dusk either between individual pairs of groups spawning in a single unit, or even both occurring simultaneously. The male initiates the affair by approaching the female and swimming by her side for a period before the pair take off slowly in unison into the water column to an explosion of sperm and eggs. The male often assumes temporary colour patterns for courtship. The spawning sequence of the Surgeonfish is a much slower process than the frantic orgasmic dash by other fishes. The Surgeonfish obviously realizes the importance of foreplay!

Group spawning for surgeonfish is very similar to that described for wrasses and parrotfish. Prior to spawning the group gathers along the outer edge of the reef flirting with each other whilst gradually forming tighter groups. Eventually in response to some unseen signal they dash to the surface in parallel formation and at the peak of the ascent shed eggs and gametes. Spawning ascents often occur throughout the school simultaneously, which must be quite an impressive sight to see. Hatching occurs typically just over 24 hours later (26 hours at 24C water temperature), the larvae found well offshore. They have a long planktonic stage of a few months before full adolescence is reached.

Shooting SURGEONFISHES

The group Surgeonfish have erratic swimming movements while the schooling type are fast swimmers. These make life rather difficult for the photographer. Locate their feeding ground and catch them feeding from a distance of 2m(6ft) or find them at night for some close up portrait. The 60mm macro lens is highly recommended. My favorites are the Striped Surgeonfish (*Acanthurus lineatus*) and Number 6 Blue Surgeonfish (*Paracanthurus hepatus*).

Convict surgeonfish
Acanthurus triostegus
20cm Indo-Pacific
Ari Atoll, Maldives
60mm f11 1/60sec

White-margin unicornfish
Naso annulatus
100cm Indo Pacific
Layang Layang, Malaysia
60mm f8 1/60sec

Vlaming unicornfish
Naso vlamingii
55cm, Indo-Pacific
GBR, Australia
60mm f11 1/60sec

Surgical sharp spine at tail-base.

Striped surgeonfish
Acanthurus lineatus
38cm, Indo-Pacific
Manado-Tua, Nth Sulawesi
60mm f11 1/60sec

Getting to Know TRIGGERFISHES

Triggerfish are definitely one of the most distinctive and highly evolved fish that live on coral reefs; they are the cousins of Filefishes (*Monacanthidae*), Porcupinefishes (*Diodontidae*), Boxfishes *(Ostraciidae)* and Puffers (*Tetraodontidae*). Often seen cruising blithesomely along the reef, the Triggerfish derives its name from the ability to lock its first dorsal fin in an erect position when wedging itself in holes, snout first. The second spine acts like a trigger of a handgun; depressing it this releases the cocked position of the first spine.

Closely related to the Filefish family the Triggerfish family consists of 7 genera and about 35 species, many of which have complex patterns. They are recognizable by their oval fish platter shape, small eyes high on the head, and a small beaky mouth with long chisel-like teeth like that of a rabbit. A large heavy bodied fish it attains 75cm(30") in some of the larger species. The 2nd dorsal fin and anal fins are almost identical in size, which gives a side-profile appearance of only two recognizable fins on each side of the body. These are their swimming fins and their tail fin is only used when speed or quick evasive action is required.

Domain of TRIGGERFISHES

Triggerfishes are reef dwellers and generally tend to be solitary creatures found throughout the Indo-Pacific. Most of the smaller species are shy, especially the Luminous Blue triggerfish *(Odonus niger)*, which will dive for cover almost instantaneously when approached by a diver. When evading predators, they will use their trigger mechanism to wedge themselves tightly in holes and crevices until the danger has passed. For a safe nights' sleep they are found in the same position, with only their tail hanging out of small holes.

Eat or Be Eaten

Feeding on a wide variety of marine animals the triggerfish uses its powerful jaws and teeth to crunch hard shelled species such as crabs, sea urchins, molluscs and even coral into little digestible pieces. Each jaw is equipped with the ideal crunching and munching tools with 8 long protruding incisors in an outer row buttressed by a secondary inner row of 6 teeth.

Clown triggerfish
Balistoides conspicillum
45cm E Indian to W Pacific
Sipadan, Malaysia
60mm f11 1/60sec

Gilded triggerfish
Xanthichthys auromarginatus
20cm, Indo-Pacific
Coral Sea, Australia
60mm f8, 1/125sec

Red-tooth triggerfish
Odonus niger
38cm, common , Indo-Pacific
Maaya Thila, Maldives
60mm f11 1/60sec

In Bed with Triggerfishes

In contrast to most fishes who disperse their eggs in the open sea, Triggerfish are one of the few fish families who practice parental care. Recent research has shown that in contrast to the other families that practice parental care - Blennies, Damselfishes and Gobies families, it is the male that guards the eggs, whilst in triggerfishes tradition, the female assumes the maternal role (Frick 1980). Nests are usually shallow craters between 50-80cm(20-30") in diameter found in the sand or rubble. The female prepares the nest by ejecting jets of water from her mouth to clear the sand and removing rubble with her jaws.

Spawning takes place before dawn after a brief courtship by the male swimming between the nest site and the female's sleeping quarters. The eggs are laid in the nest and fertilized in a concentrated mass. The female then guards them until they hatch. With an incubation period of less than 24 hours the female triggerfish has a better deal in comparison to other fish families that practice parental care. Juvenile triggerfishes are not as brilliantly coloured as the adults.

Beware, some triggerfishes have a worse reputation than sharks, especially the Titan Triggerfish during nesting season. Should an intruder approach the vicinity of their nest, these normally passive fish turn violently aggressive. Not only aggressive to other fish that try and eat their eggs this behaviour is often extended to any unwary diver that happens to swim past her nest. Often this behaviour just consists of a darting quick movement towards the intruder, then quickly retreating back to the nest. There have been many reports of divers that have actually been attacked. One of my experiences of an attack by a Titan Triggerfish *(Balistoides viridescens)* occurred during a dive off Bunaken Island in North Sulawesi. Out of the blue, I saw a 70cm size fish rushing at me with teeth protruding like a mad doberman. A series of swift attacks ensued. Eventually after 8 attempts, the fish withdrew without any injury sustained to either party. Triggerfish are capable of inflicting huge bruises and severe lacerations removing small chunks of flesh that require surgical stitches. Some of the bigger species of Triggerfish have a bad reputation, namely the Yellow-spotted *(Pseudobalistes fuscus)* and the Titan Triggerfish, and it is recommended that you should grant them their due respect. If a large stationary fish is facing you in your direction of travel, alter course to avoid confrontation. This could be a female guarding her nest.

Shooting Triggerfishes

It is pretty hard to shoot a good picture of a triggerfish. You will either find them wedged into small crevices, out of range, or when you are too busy fending them off with your cameras. If you do find one that co-operates, make sure you finish the roll off! I got lucky with one that was busy at lunch with a Spanish dancer nudibranch and expended a whole roll of film on a very contended Triggerfish.

Yellow-margin triggerfish
Pseudobalistes flavimarginatus
<u>60cm</u> E Indian to W Pacific
Mabul, Malaysia
60mm f8 1/125sec

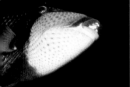

Titan triggerfish
Balistoides viridescens
<u>75ee</u>cm, Indo-Pacific
Palau
60mm f11, 1/125sec

Pink-tail triggerfish
Melichthys vidua
<u>35cm</u>, Indo-Pacific
Maldives
60mm f11 1/60sec

Moorish Idol — Zanclidae

Getting to Know the MOORISH IDOL

Looking much like a bandit in daylight, the Moorish Idol (*Zanclus cornutus*) is one of the most prominent and frequently seen members of the coral reef community. Its distinctively flowing extended dorsal fin; bright yellow and white colours and black stripes will quickly capture the attention of any reef watcher. The Moorish idol is a single species family. Its popularity among divers and snorkellers has earned it a special place in this book.

The Moorish Idol's extremely long flowing and filamentous third dorsal spine arising from its back, has caused it to be mistaken for the Common and Schooling Bannerfish (*Heniochus acuminatus* and *Heniochus diphreutes*) which also don similar extended dorsal fins. On careful observation, however, the moorish idol is distinctly different to a bannerfish in its strongly pointed long snout with a yellow bridge and its black bar colouring. Two black vertical bars flow from the nape to abdomen and a second bar through the rear dorsal and anal fins (See picture opposite). An adult moorish idol is also identified by its small bony projection in front of the eyes. Being a close relative of the Surgeonfish (*Acanthuridae*) they inherit a deep strongly compressed body, giving a flat profile, with equal sized dorsal and anal fins.

Domain of the MOORISH IDOL

Often found in pairs or small groups in the shallow water of a coral reef they have been reported to venture down to abyssal depths of over 180m(600ft).

Eat or Be Eaten

Though omnivorous feeders, they prefer to use their long snout to pick at sponges and coral bits rather than their algae menu.

In Bed with the Moorish Idol

Although it is one of the most popular fish seen by divers, amazingly there have been no reports of any courtship or spawning activities of the Moorish idol. Scientists assume that they most likely spawn at dusk and know that they produce pelagic eggs. Often observed in twosomes in the late afternoon this might suggest that they spawn in pairs rather than being group sex participants.

Shooting the Moorish Idol

Moorish Idols are not camera shy. Although frequently on the move, snap shots of your favorite fish can easily be captured with a 60mm or 24mm - 35mm lens for a group picture.

Moorish Idol
Zanclus cornutus
22cm Indo-Pacific
Mabul, Malaysia
60mm f11 1/60sec

Moorish Idol
Zanclus cornutus
22cm Indo-Pacific
Semilan, Thailand
24mm f8 1/60sec

Check out the
similarity to
Longfin bannerfish
Heriochus acuminatus
60mm f11 1/125sec

Getting to Know FILEFISHES

Monacanthidae is the closest relative of the Triggerfish *(Balistidae)* and they are often mistaken for one another. Filefishes would not be amused as they are a more diverse lot and in the fish world they would regard themselves as intellectually superior to their cousins because of their chameleonic skills. Filefishes appear to be similar to triggerfishes with their compressed body and a strong upright first dorsal spine, which can be used to wedge themselves into coral crevices. However, the body of a Filefish is generally more compressed with a pointed snout and they have a few less incisor teeth. Filefish are referred to as Leatherjackets in Australia because of their tough leathery skin. They have the ability to change the colour of this tough skin to blend into their habitat and in some species additional tassels and appendages are developed to provide additional camouflage. The diversity of the size and shape of filefishes varies enormously. The tiny diamond shaped Pygmy Leatherjacket *(Brachaluteres jacksonianus)* is only 3cm(1.5") long whilst the beautiful greenish coloured Scribbled Filefish *(Aluterus scriptus)* is 1m(36") long and has a compressed triggerfish shape. There is also the Mimic Filefish *(Paraluteres prionurus)* who fools its predator by mimicking the colour and shape of a poisonous Pufferfish *(Canthigaster valentini)*. With the exception of the missing dorsal spine in the latter, both the fishes are almost identical in shape and colour pattern.

Domain of FILEFISHES

Filefishes are small to medium sized fish and 65 of the family of about 80 species can found in the cooler Australian waters. The coral reef species lead a secretive life hiding among gorgonian fans, sea grass and *Acropora* corals. In the day they can be found alone, in pairs or in schools foraging the reef to satisfy their omnivorous diet. They feed on a great variety of food from benthic animals to plant life. The Longnose Coral Filefish *(Oxymonacanthus longirostris)* with yellow polka dots on a light blue body is almost exclusively found in pairs wandering among hard coral plates. They are assumed to be monogamous and they are one of the most beautiful ornamental reef fishes.

In Bed with Filefishes

Spawning is assumed to be similar to that of the Triggerfish, laying demersal eggs (Refer to the *Balistidae* section)

Shooting Filefishes

Most Filefishes are slow swimmers but the problem is that they are always hiding among sea grass or deep inside coral crevices. I adopt the 'lucky shot' attitude when taking pictures of them. The key to success is lots of bottom time, lots of film and of course using the right lens.

Bristle-tailed filefish
Acreichthys tomentosus
7cm Indo-Pacific
Semilan, Thailand
105mm f16 1/60sec

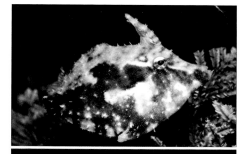

Scribbled filefish
Aluterus scriptus
1m common Indo Pacific
Derawan, Indonesia
60mm f11 1/60sec

Mimic filefish
Paraluteres prionurus
*10*cm, Indo-Pacific
mimic *Canthigaster valentini*
Kimbe Bay, PNG
105mm f16 1/60sec

Beaked leatherjacket
Oxymonacanthus longirostris
8cm, E. Africa to Samoa
GBR, Australia
105mm f11 1/60sec

Getting to Know BARRACUDAS

Among the top predators of the ocean, barracudas' sleek elongated, cylindrical, silvery bodies resemble small mean torpedoes. Barracudas belong to the single genus Sphyraenidae family with only 20 species and are found only in tropical water. People that describe the barracuda as the meanest critter on the reef are perhaps intimidated by their pointed snout and protruding lower jaw. This large mouth is filled with an awesome array of long razor sharp teeth. With small fins and a forked tail, their silvery elongated body with dark bars or chevron markings radiates an aura of a vicious predator. Medium to large fish, they grow to 2m(6.6ft). Large solitary species like the *Sphyraena barracuda*, have a habit of approaching a diver at close range out of curiosity. Despite looking fierce they are generally harmless as their diet consists primarily of fish and sea jellies. However, have due respect for the Barracuda, as they have been known to snap hand spears in half and bite through propeller blades!

Domain of BARRACUDAS

Young barracudas believe strongly in safety in numbers and schooling for survival. We often find them hanging out at the outer edge of a reef, and sometimes the schools are so enormous that it is like swimming through a solid curtain of silver. They look like precision swimming machines moving in exact co-ordination, exactly the same speed and distance from each other. If any member of the school detects danger, their slightest change in direction will cause an immediate chain reaction throughout the whole school. We once observed an Oceanic white tip shark trying to pluck the last swimming member of a school. The entire school immediately changed direction to face the shark and at the same time closed ranks and contracted to form one big silvery mass. The shark turned on its fins and disappeared.

In Bed with BARRACUDAS

Though little is known about the Barracuda's courtship or spawning affairs, they are assumed to generally migrate to a specific spawning site in groups of large numbers (e.g. Johannes 1981). Mating in schools has its advantage, as the close physical proximity of males and females makes fertilization of eggs more efficient. It would not be wrong to ascertain that their eggs are pelagic and the juveniles are known to be voracious small fish eaters. They also attack moving plankton and are aggressive towards one another. In some species fully mature adults leave the school, returning only for mating. Some adults of The Great Barracuda *(Sphyraena barracuda)* for example, are generally solitary and territorial except during mating season and often found hanging out on reef flats.

Shooting BARRACUDAS

The problem is having the right lens at the right time. Most often you can slowly merge into a school, which is a wild and adrenalin pumping experience. Due to their silvery body, shut down your strobe to 1/2 power and aim for the sky.

Chevron barracuda
Sphyraena qenie
90m common Indo Pacific
Derawan, Indonesia
20mm f8 1/60sec

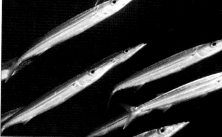

Heller's barracuda
Sphyraena helleri
68cm Western Pacific
Pohnpei
15mm f11 1/60sec

Check out those teeth!
Great barracuda
Sphyraena barracuda
1.7m, E. Africa to Hawaii
Dinah's Beach, PNG
60mm f11 1/60sec

Great barracuda
Sphyraena barracuda
1.7m, E. Africa to Hawaii
Ruang Nth Sulawesi
28mm f11 1/60sec

Getting to Know PUFFERFISHES

On the reef the Pufferfish is the more lovable cousin of the Porcupinefis (*Diodontidae*), especially when seen resting among leathery soft coral looking like puppy dog or a fur seal. An oddball in appearance it has the bizarre ability to instantl inflate itself to ward off predators. Puffed up and looking more like a small footba waddling away from its predator the Pufferfish, or Blowfish, is often described a "cute".

Most pufferfish are small to medium sized fish with scaleless skin, a beak-like mouth, single short dorsal fin at the lower back and a similar sized anal fin below. Withou pelvic fins to support their body, pufferfish are only seen resting among sponges an soft corals. Some species don complex colour patterns but most of them are relativel drab in colour.

A family of over 100 species the reef pufferfishes can be subdivided into two distinc groups; the sharp-nosed puffers *"Canthigaster"*, and the bulbous *"Arothron."* Th *Canthigaster* group are very small, rarely exceeding 12cm(5") in length, with a lon sharp snout and typically colourful and striped. They are often found at the base c coral heads and crevices. The *Arothron* are larger, more rotund and solid with a seal like appearance.

When provoked or frightened, the pufferfish discourages would-be predators b increasing its body size by pumping water into an elastic abdominal sac from the ventra part of its stomach. To further deter advances from its predator, the pufferfish als releases, through its skin, a powerful poison called Tetraodontoxin, which is produce in its liver and ovaries. The potent Tetraodontoxin is much stronger than cyanide Found in the internal organs, it is responsible for a number of deaths each year i eastern Asia where the fish is eaten. It is rumoured that the toxins used by th boogieman in Haiti, to turn men into zombies, are those of the pufferfish! I underwater encounters the pufferfish is harmless and any attempts to frighten it, s that it inflates itself, are considered un-cool.

Domain of PUFFERFISHES

Pufferfishes can be found worldwide in all tropical and temperate habitats from coral and rocky reefs to seagrass beds and estuaries. The benthic reef dwellers are nocturnal and unassuming by nature, living in coral, rocks and sand, at the outer edge of the reef during the day. Most live in pairs or in small aggregations.

Star puffer
Arothron stellatus
90 cm Indo Pacific
Layang Layang, Malaysia
28mm f11 1/60sec

False eye toby
Canthigaster papua
9cm Indo Australasia Arch.
GBR, Australia
60mm f11 1/125sec

Black saddled toby
Canthigaster valentini
9cm, widespread Indo-Pacific
GBR, Australia
60mm f11 1/60sec

Map puffer
Arothron mappa
60cm, E. Africa to Samoa
Maldives
60mm f11 1/60sec

Eat or Be Eaten

Sharing the same varied diet as their spiny cousin, the Porcupinefish, they use their teeth to crush the shells of their largely crustaceous diet.

In Bed with the Puffers

Many Pufferfish are group spawners, laying demersal adhesive eggs, which may or may not be tended by the male. Not much is known about the spawning of the genus *Arothron* but research has been completed on the spawning habits of the genus *Canthigaster*. There is thought to be a three-tiered social system consisting of solitary members, pairs and harem groups within *Canthigaster* (Gladstone). Within the harem there are between 4-7 females and one dominant male who defends the territories of the group. Spawning takes place each morning and the male selectively chooses a different female from his harem each day. The female picks the spawning site, typically either a tuft of algae on a piece of coral or a shallow depression in the sand.

Courtship lasts up to 35 minutes in which the male follows the female with displays of exaggerated swimming, nudging her abdomen before she settles on to her nest. There she lays her stomach across the nest and in a few seconds lays hundreds of eggs whilst the male lies across or beside her and fertilizes them, departing immediately after a quick 'wham bang, thank you maam'. The female only remains at the nest site for a few minutes longer than the male, pressing and fanning the eggs before leaving and continuing her daily routine. The incubation period is from 4 days upwards depending on water temperature, after which the larvae swim freely before settling on the bottom upon reaching adolescence.

Shooting Pufferfishes

Pufferfishes are easily photographed when they are found resting almost motionless among corals and sponges during the day and night. You can approach pretty close without them being frightened away. Catching them on the move is a little trickier, but it is possible to pre-empt their moves after a short period of observation.

Bennett's toby
Canthigaster bennetti
<u>10 cm</u> Indo Pacific
Tulamben, Bali
105mm f11 1/60sec

Normal phase

Black spotted puffer
Arothron nigropunctatus
<u>25cm</u> E Africa to Samoa
Maldives
60mm f11 1/60sec

Bi-color phase

Seagrass puffer
Arothron immaculatus
<u>28</u>cm, Indian Ocean
Bali, Secret Bay
60mm f11 1/125sec

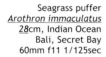

Stars & Stripes puffer
Arothron hispidus
<u>48cm</u>, Indo-Pacific
Tukang Besi, Indonesia
60mm f11 1/60sec

Moray Eels Muraenidae

Getting to Know Eels

Since being sensationalized in the movie "The Deep", moray eels have an ill reputation. Their status as ferocious killers that stalk and attack divers is a load of garb. Nothing could be further from the truth. Moray eels are shy and retiring animals that lead a secret life beneath the chambers of the sea. There are 110 species world-wide.

Moray Eels are distinctive and easily identifiable by their disposition, color, pattern and their body size. Looking more like a snake with its elongated muscularly compressed body, the eel is actually a fish with one long ribbon dorsal fin, which often melts into the anal fins and tail, and no pectoral fins.

Among fishes however they are 'odd balls'. The vertical slit gills of other fish are replaced with a couple of holes on each side of their body situated several inches behind their small head. With two protruding tubular nostrils moray eels possess an advance sensory sense of smell. They are also equipped with long fang-like canine teeth and their scaleless body is covered with mucus. Just like their earthier counterparts they swim in a zig-zag motion like that of a snake grazing in the grass.

Colour and size variations range from the Green Giant Moray (G. javanicus), which can reach 220cm(8.5ft) in length and weigh about 29kg(63 lbs), to the beautiful, extremely elongated, fluorescent blue Ribbon Eel (Rhinomuraena quaesita) which only reach a maximum length of 65cm(30")

Domain of Eels

Moray eels are found in holes and small crevices among corals and rubble with their head poking out of their lair. They seem to be singing a silent song with their mouth opening and closing; actually they are inhaling water, passing water through their gills and gill holes. It is this open mouth breathing technique, with their sharp canine teeth fully visible to the observer that earns them their ferocious reputation.

Morays are fairly docile and non-aggressive but they will bite when harassed and quite understandably they are known to fiercely defend their castles and their lives. Putting your hand into their domain, among holes and caves, is an invasion of their privacy and most likely you will be attacked. Once bitten your natural reaction of pulling your finger or hand out from their mouth of fanged teeth will result in severe lacerations requiring surgical stitches. In this situation it is better to stay still, wait for their mouth to open again on its own accord (which it has to do to breathe) and you will probably suffer only a few puncture wounds instead. There are songs written about Moray eels!

Feeding moray eels is an invitation for trouble. Reputed to have bad eyesight they often mistake your ears, nose and hair for morsels of food.

Whitemouth moray
Gymnothorax meleagris
1m, Indo-Pacific
Bunaken, Nth Sulawesi
60mm f11, 1/60sec

Ribbon eel
(female is yellow,
juvenile is black)
Rhinomuraena quaesita
3cm, Indo-Australasia Arch.
Bunaken, Nth Sulawesi
60mm f11 1/60sec

Giant moray
Gymnothorax javanicus
3m, widespread Indo-Pacific
Maldives
28mm f11 1/60sec

Eat or Be Eaten

Eels live a solitary life only leaving their lair to roam the reef at night in search of food. Carnivorous by nature they feed on octopus, shrimps, mussels, lobsters, and small fish. Some moray eels have developed pharngeal jaws that allow them to crush the hard shells of mussels, clams and crustaceans.

When fish is on the menu, they use their fanged teeth to firmly grip their food. Without chewing the fish, they re-position the fish to point towards their throat head first. This prevents the fish's dorsal fins from sticking in their throat and choking them. In one "whoosh" the entire fish is swallowed whole and the moray will spend the rest of the evening digesting its meal. We once witnessed a giant moray swallowing a porcupine fish in one gulp - boy what a stomach ache he must have had that evening!

Morays are also known to be scavengers of dead fish and they often attempt to enter fish pods for a free feed on fish bait.

In Bed with Moray Eels ...slippery

The reproductive behaviour of Eels is a well kept secret. Complete accounts and observations of mating pairs are too few to be conclusive. Courtship behaviour is believed to vary between genera and includes swimming singularly or in groups near the surface. On one occasion we sighted a pair of white spotted morays (possibly *G. meleagris*) entwined on the bottom of a reef flat in North Sulawesi). In conjunction with the accounts published by G Brocks and Yamamoto (1972) a possible scenario would suggest that a pair of eels leave their holes and slowly approach one another on the reef bottom. There they possibly stop at eels length, together raise their body, with their mouths open and dorsals erected. After a brief puff of silent songs they will embrace and finally fall back to lie on the bottom entwined, ultimately pressing their abdomens together and releasing a cloud of gametes at the height of their communion. They are also reputed to be very territorial during breeding season and will attack unprovoked.

Shooting Moray Eels

Morays will often retreat into their hole when approached quickly. Stop at a short distance and let them become accustomed to your presence and acquaint them with your strobes by firing off a few frames. With a little gentle encouragement they are great for close up photographs. As a nocturnal fish, they are livelier at night and a full body shot is possible then.

Spot-face moray
Gymnothorax fimbriatus
50cm,Indo-Australasia to
Micronesia, South Japan
Ambon, Indonesia
60mm f11, 1/125sec

White-eyed moray
Siderea thyrsoidea
*80*cm,Indo-Pacific
Labuan, Malaysia
60mm f11 1/125sec

far left
Harlequin snake eel
possibly *Callechelys sp.*
Indo-Australasia Arch.
Mabul, Malaysia
60mm f11 1/60sec

left
Black spotted moray
Gymnothorax favagineus
with cleaner wrasse
:m,widespread Indo-Pacific
Maldives
60mm f11 1/125sec

Squirrelfishes Holocentridae

Getting to Know SQUIRRELFISHES

If you see a red fish beneath a coral ledge or cave with ridiculously big round bulbous eyes, it is probably a Squirrelfish or a Soldierfish. Little is known about the Squirrelfish family but it would not be wrong to assume that they derived their common name from their large eyes or that it is so called because of their timid nature and ability to dart away and hide the first sign of danger, characteristics of their land counterparts.

Often a prolific sight at night, Squirrelfishes and Soldierfishes are among the most abundant of the nocturnally active reef fishes. From a family of 70 species in 8 genera, their red colour, or shades thereof, and large eyes make them easily recognizable. The species Big-eye or Scarlet Soldierfish (Myripristis pralinia) is commonly observed on reefs and they have the biggest eyes in the family. Other clues of identification include their large rough scales, pronounced forked tail, and a relatively large mouth. They are medium fish generally between 15-35cm(6-15").

The species of the Sargocentron genus of squirrelfish are usually striped, often territorial, and their defence system includes a large spine at the corner of the preopercle that is lacking in Soldierfishes. Though not as severe as of that a Scorpionfish (Scorpaenidae), the Squirrelfish's spine is venomous and can inflict painful wounds if provoked. We once witnessed a diver suffer temporary paralysis for 4 hours after suffering a wound of this nature.

Domain of SQUIRRELFISHES

Most species are found in shallow waters on rocky bottoms or coral reefs in tropical waters up to 30m(100ft) although some live in depths of up to 200m(656ft). They can be found in most tropical waters around the world, especially near the equator, though some species prefer the cooler sub-tropical waters.

Their large eyes suggest most species are nocturnal. During the day they will elude the underwater observer by hiding in caves or crevices or under ledges. They emerge at night and swim either in pairs or small to large groups foraging for food along the reef. An unusual sight, you may occasionally see them swimming upside down beneath coral plates and caverns.

Whitetip squirrelfish
Myripristis vittata
20cm, Indo-Pacific
Bunaken, Nth Sulawesi
60mm f11, 1/60sec

Blood-drop squirrelfish
Neoniphon sammara
2cm, Indo-Australasia Arch.
Davao, Philippines
60mm f11 1/125sec

Smallmouth squirrelfish
Sargocentron microstoma
:m, widespread Indo-Pacific
Coral Sea, Australia
60mm f11 1/60sec

Squirrelfishes Holocentridae

Eat of Be Eaten
Squirrelfish and Soldierfish sustain their life by feeding on small fishes and invertebrates. Exceptions to the rule include the genus of Myripristis, which feeds on larger elements of plankton whilst the genus of Sargocentron mainly feed on benthic crabs and shrimps.

In Bed with SQUIRRELFISHES
Little is known about the rituals of courtship and the sexual activity of Squirrelfish. Except for a few observations of possible courtship behaviour nothing is conclusive. Since they are usually found in small groups, it may not be too far out to suggest that they participate in group spawning at dusk or in the early evening.

Shooting SQUIRRELFISHES
Squirrelfish are best photographed at night while they are our foraging the reef. Approach cautiously to avoid spooking them into holes. Use a slow speed film, such as Fuji Velvia to bring out their colors.

Yellowstriped squirrelfish
Neoniphon aurolineatus
m, Indo-Pacific- deep water
greater than 40m rare
Enewetak Atoll, Marshall Is.
60mm f11, 1/125 sec

One spot squirrelfish
Myripristis adusta
35cm, Indo-Pacific
South Male, Maldives
60mm f11 1/60sec

Three-spot squirrelfish
Sargocentron cornutum
2.5m, South Pacific
Solomon Is
60mm f11 1/60sec

Cardinalfishes Apogonidae

Getting to Know CARDINALFISHES

After sundown Cardinalfishes come out to play. Although only small in size they certainly make up for it in numbers and variety. Predominantly silvery and translucent like they are like Christmas lights flickering on the coral reefs at night. Their common name, derived from their red coloration, is very misleading as a huge number of the species are yellow, brown, black, blue and silver tints to goldish orange.

Important characteristics of the cardinalfish are its large scales and large mouth designed for brooding offspring. Their bodies are laterally compressed with two separate dorsal fins and a long tail base. Particular species are easily identifiable by distinctive markings of stripes, spots, and colouration. Most of them are lightly coloured and a few species have bacterial luminescent organs, which makes them glow in the dark.

Cardinalfishes are among the smallest fish in the ocean, reaching a maximum length of 22cm(10"). There are about 250 species in 23 genera worldwide. The majority of them are found in the Indo-Pacific basin. Most species belong to the genus Apogon and generally can be found during the day beneath corals, in sandy reef lagoons, in crevices of deep slopes among coral trees, and shipwrecks. Some species are known to inhabit ledges in deeper water. A few smaller species are known to have developed close living arrangements with other toxic animals such as the Urchin Cardinal (*Sphaeramia versicolor*) that lives among sea urchins (Eibl-Eibesfeldt), and the Crown-of-Thorns Cardinal (*Siphamia fuscolineata*) who lives with the Crown of Thorns sea star (Allen 1972).

Domain of CARDINAL FISHES

Cardinalfishes rest together during the day, but when evening comes they will either wander the reef alone or split off in small groups or pairs. Some species (Rhabdamia species - a semi transparent species) congregate in thousands and they generally stay within a wreck or reef corridors.

Cardinalfishes are the nocturnal equivalent of the daytime Damselfishes (Pomacentridae). If you see a fish wandering about in the open at night, it will probably be a cardinalfish. Some species prefer to dine alongside basketstars and gorgonian fans.

Moluccen cardinalfish
Apogon moluccensis
9cm, East Indies to
Australia
Bali, Indonesia
105mm f16 1/25sec

Threadfin cardinalfish
Sphaeramia nematoptera
7cm, Eat Indies to
Nth. Australia
Togian Is. Central Sulawesi
105mm f16 1/60sec

Blackstriped cardinalfish
Apogon nigrofasciatus
8cm, common Red Sea
to Australia
Alor, Indonesia
105mm f22 1/60sec

Capricorn cardinalfish
Apogon capricornis
8cm, Capricorn Reef
Australia
Milne Bay, PNG
105mm f22 1/60sec

Cardinalfishes Apogonidae

Eat or Be Eaten

Diet varies from species to species and consists of zooplankton and small benthic animals such as small shrimps and crabs.

In Bed with Cardinalfishes

In the society of Apogon Cardinalfishes it is the female who initiates the lengthy courtship, which may sometimes take all night. Once a female who is 'on heat' has selected her partner she will begin the courtship by swimming closely by his side. The pair will soon move in a circular pattern with her on the outside and the male on the inside. Should they be interrupted they will both split off, but quickly return to their circling behaviour. This may continue through the night and gradually with increasing passion the male will wrap his anal fins around his companions abdomen (Garnaud 1960).

The pair quivering side by side as masses of egg balls are released by the female and simultaneously fertilized by the male signals the height of the union. Cardinalfish eggs are gelatinous and bound together in a tight ball.

Just when you think that they have a better deal, it is the responsibility of the male to tend to his offspring by engulfing them in his mouth. A swollen throat region easily distinguishes a brooding father and the eggs can be seen when he periodically juggles to aerate them. During the incubation period, from 8-17 days, the male starves while the female stands by to defend her brooding companion. After hatching the larvae remain in the planktonic layer for several weeks before settling on the reef.

Shooting Cardinalfishes

Approaching these little 'razzle dazzles' of the reef is not a problem at night. They will generally remain still and pose while you settle down to compose your picture. Watch strobe positioning as their colouration tends to be reflective. Flaring occurs when the fish are moving especially during group pictures.

Ring-tail cardinalfish
Apogon aureus
<u>12</u>cm, East Africa to
West Pacific
Tioman, Malaysia
105mm f16 1/125sec

Five-lined cardinalfish
Cheilodipterus quinquelineatus
<u>12</u>cm, East Africa to
Polynesia
Palau
105mm f16 1/60sec

Cheek-bar cardinalfish
Apogon sealei
<u>8</u>cm, Indonesia to
Phllippines
Sangie, Nth Sulawesi
105mm f22 1/60sec

Yellow-striped cardinalfish
Apogon cyanosoma
<u>8</u>cm, East Africa to
Australia
Derawan, Indonesia
105mm f22 1/60sec

Jawfishes Opistognathidae

Getting to Know JAWFISHES

An incognito among coral reef fishes and the moles of the underworld, Jawfishes live in underground burrows on open reef patches. Its secretive lifestyle has evaded discoveries of but a few known species. There are probably quite a few of them scurrying around beneath the world's oceans but now that the secret is out, new species are being identified regularly. Jawfishes have a big mouth and an enlarged toady head. Besides being used for sustaining life, their big mouth is an essential tool for home building and indeed for ensuring the very continuity of their species, by providing an in built incubator. They possess a pair of big round bulging, usually black, eyes and their body colouration is mostly dullish white, grey, brown or yellow. Generally it is a small fish of less than 10cm(3") but large jawfishes have been recorded at lengths of up to 50cm(15").

In Bed With Jawfishes

Leading a secret lifestyle, Jawfishes courtship behaviour has only been vaguely recorded, however the genera Aurifrons has been studied in detail. They are sometimes assumed to mate heterogeneously at random but could also be monogamous. The Atlantic Yellow Jawfish (*Opistognathus aurifrons*) has been observed in a permanent relationship, mating regularly and helping cleaning his partners burrow, and vice versa (Colin 1972). Sexual advances are made by the male displaying courtship colours as it hovers over the female's burrow. The courting sequence varies with species but generally he hovers for 3-5 seconds before returning to his burrow. For some species this song and dance may need to be repeated every 4-5 minutes and may continue for an hour. When sufficiently aroused and ready, the female follows the male back to his burrow where spawning takes place inside. This is the only time that the female and male share the same burrow leading otherwise separate lives. It is the male who performs the maternal duties of orally brooding the eggs in his big mouth. With the eggs protruding from his jaws he ensures adequate ventilation by occasionally agitating them back and forth in his mouth. He is assumed to settle the eggs down in his burrow when taking a break for feeding time. Hatching occurs between 7 to 9 days when the male releases the eggs in the water. The larvae settle back down to the reef bottom in about 15 days where they are immediately recognizable as jawfish. At about 10mm to 15mm(1/3-5/8") in size they begin burrowing their own home.

awfishes are found living alone in their self-built burrow on the reef bed. Although they re found in individual burrows, a Jawfish community can be found with burrows situated n close proximity. Their home engineering and maintenance skills are rather complex in he world of fishes. After selecting a site they clear the area by scooping and spitting out

unwanted materials with their jaws. These powerful jaws even perform the shifting of larger rocks. Excavating the burrow then begins, again using their mouth. Once the burrow is complete the final stage involves building a wall of neatly stacked pebbles, coral pieces or shells around their fortress. A home is built in about 8 hours and if major catastrophes occur causing their home to collapse, home building or restructuring begins immediately. If you

ee a Jawfish away from its burrow, they are often leaving home to gather raw materials reinforce their fortress, or dumping unwanted fragments into their neighbours' ackyard. When not performing their domestic chores, time is spent at the entrance of e burrow feeding on passing planktonic or benthic invertebrates. As one would assume r someone that has built their own home, they are extremely territorial and will gorously defend the vicinity of their burrow. The Gold Rim Jawfish (*Opistognathus sp*) is new species still awaiting description by scientists. It is frequently sighted from Ambon, ali and Bunaken to Toli-Toli, Indonesia.

Gold-spec jawfish
Opistognathus sp.
un-described
11cm,widespread Indonesia
Toli Toli, Nth Sulawesi
this one took over 6hrs
to build his burrow.
105mm f16 1/125sec

Lizardfishes Synodontidae

Getting to know LIZARDFISHES

Lizardfishes have no fear. Their appearance reminds us of the most ancient inhabitants of the earth. Possessing a reptile-like head with a fearsome personality to match they are ferocious predators endowed with a large mouth and numerous sharp teeth. Even their tongue is lined with inward directed teeth. Sitting patiently on the reef bottom they are well camouflaged by their body colouration and sit silently poised on the reef bottom waiting for potential prey.

Its reptilian head gives a side profile similar to that of the terra-firma lizard from which its name derives. Their almost cigar-shaped body is cylindrical, moderately elongated and all its fins are spineless; a high dorsal fin is situated along the mid-body followed by barely visible small fins and forked caudal fins. Despite its primitive features of rounded scales and abdominal pelvic fins some species have surprisingly advanced features such as the buoyancy control of a swim bladder.

Their body colours match their particular habitat and provide excellent camouflage, typically silvery sandy-grey colours although they are often bright red in deep water. The Lizardfish family consists of about 40 known species in 3 genera. The largest species measures up to 60cm(27inches)and some species live at a depth of up to 400m(1320ft), although most live in the shallower waters of the reef.

Domain of LIZARDFISHES

Living alone in the sparse open sedimentary reef bottom, Lizardfishes have the ability to quickly bury themselves completely in the sandy bottom, leaving only their eyes peeping out to scan for unsuspecting prey.

Tail-blotch lizardfish
Synodus jaculum
19cm, Indo-Pacific
Milne Bay, PNG
60mm f11, 1/60sec

Two-spot lizardfish
Synodus binotatus
5cm, GBR to Malaysia
Mabul, Malaysia
60mm f11 1/60sec

Reef lizardfish
Synodus variegatus
25cm, widespread
Maldives
60mm f11 1/60sec

Lizardfishes Synodontidae

Eat or Be Eaten

All Lizardfishes are ravenous carnivores employing cryptic antics to catch their prey. Capable of darting upward in a flash to feed on small fishes they gulp and swallow the fish whole. On a few occasions they have been observed to prolong their darting efforts for the worthier prize of a larger butterflyfish for dinner. We had a unique experience watching a Javelin Lizardfish (possibly Synodus jaculum) successfully leaping up to about 1m(3ft) to catch a 3cm(1 1/2") Sabretooth Bluestriped Blenny (Plagiotremus rhinorhynchos) in mid-water for lunch. Settling ferociously at the bottom the blenny was swallowed whole in 3 gulps. In the next instance, a mate of the ill-fated blenny took revenge by latching on to the underside of the lizardfish's jaw with its fangs.

The fearsome predator who had now turned prey was next seen swimming frantically to shake the pest off its jaw. The bold blenny eventually detached itself but only after it had successfully reeked revenge by taking a huge chunk of tissue off its victim.

In Bed with Lizardfishes

Lizardfishes indulge in prolonged courtship before spawning with their partners. Courtship occurs throughout the day with the male actively pursuing a female companion. Whenever she stops, he will attempt to sit in front of her with gills fully flared showing his courtship colours. Sometimes he can be seen sitting side by side or across her. Once she has submitted to his persistent pursuit, the pair can be seen making lengthy and elaborate movements along the reef flat. The male will stay and defend her until she is ready to spawn.

Spawning occurs at dusk, with the pair ascending about 5m(16.5ft) off the bottom simultaneously to eject clouds of elongated pelagic eggs, which take about 3-4 days to develop into skinny larva.

Shooting Lizardfishes

Taking pictures of a fish has never been easier. Lizardfishes sit still whilst having their portrait taken. Both night and day you can locate them in their open reef habitat and just settle gently in front of them to start your photo session. Making a picture of them during mating season or feeding time requires a very fast lens and lots of frustration.

Red-marbled lizardfish
Synodus rubromarmoratus
2cm, Indo-Australasian Arch.
Rincha, Indonesia
105mm f11, 1/60sec

Tail-blocth lizardfish
feeding on Fangblenny.
Synodus jaculum
20cm Widespread
Bunaken Nth Sulawesi
105mm f11 1/60sec

Greystreak lizardfish
Synodus dermatogenys
feeding on shrimpgoby
22cm, Indo-Pacific
Kepalai, Malaysia
60mm f11 1/60sec

Getting to Know Anglerfishes

Anglerfishes, often referred to as frog-fishes have faces so ugly that only a mother could love them; but avant-garde fish photographers are attracted to them like bees to honey, traveling to remote corners of the world in search of the most hairy and ugliest frogfish. There is truth in the saying; beauty is in the eye of the beholder.

Because frogfishes are masters of ingenious camouflage, they are often difficult to find and even tougher to identify. Characterised by their lumpy sponge like shape, variously provided with warts and filaments, they have ability to change colour in days or in hours assimilating to their environ almost exactly (usually stones with bright patches of algae, sponges and sessile invertebrates). They will even adapt by growing appendages resembling algae and sponges. Through the years, their kin have fooled many scientists who described them into 165 named species. However, recently a zoologist, Theodore Pietsch got the wiser of them, putting them into their place with a classification of 4 species in 12 genera found in most tropical and temperate waters.

Charateristics of frogfishes include a large head and mouth, foot-like pectoral fins with which they can "walk" across bottom, and a narrow tube like gill opening just behind the pectoral.

Domain of Anglerfishes

Though a deep water species *Phrynichthys wedli* have been found in 1000m, frogfishes generally live in shallow water, but because of their cryptic behavior, they are often overlooked even by experienced observers. Size varies from the 10 cm Clown anglerfish to the 50cm, gienormous *Antennarius commersonii*.

Eat or Be Eaten

Anglerfishes are so named for the presence of a slender bating device of which they use to bait potential prey. Located just ahead of the dorsal fin, on their forehead, the bait known as the illicium, is angled forward over the mouth and is variously wriggled jerked or waved at potential prey. Their angling technique is deliberate, the shape colour and movement of their bait remarkably life-like imitating worms, hopping crustaceans even undulating tiny fish. Study by highspeed camera has shown that an unsuspecting would be predator is caught within less than 100th of a second. Anglerfishes are voracious carnivores; their large oblique mouths lined with rows of conical teeth capable of devouring prey twice their own size.

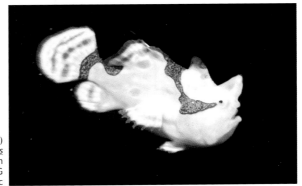

Clown anglerfish (juvenile)
Antennarius maculatus
1cm, Uncommon
Milne Bay, PNG
105mm f22 1/125sec

Clown anglerfish (adult)
Antennarius maculatus
5cm, Uncommon
Derawan Is. Indonesia
60mm f22 1/60sec

White-finger anglerfish
Antennarius nummiferi
8cm, Uncommon
Lembeh Strait Indonesia
60mm f16 1/60sec

Anglerfishes Antennariidae

In Bed with Anglerfishes

As in most animals, the female anglerfish arouses her male when she is in heat; a swollen abdomen suggests that she is ripe for the picking. Potential suitors become unusually attentive, rarely leaving the female's vicinity. Occasionally he will circle the female and repeatedly nudge and 'feel' her abdomen with his hand-like pectoral fins. Shortly before spawning the female becomes extremely distended and she floats tail-up into the water. The male becomes exaggeratedly excited, nudging her abdomen continuously. Both of them will quiver sporadically as they move towards the surface to shed of eggs and sperm. Most frogfishes release gelatinous floating egg rafts or veils, in which the eggs are embedded until hatching.   Depending on species, miniature frogfishes settle onto the reef in between 6 to 21 days. Whilst parenting ends at spawning for most frogfishes, some species like the *Antennarius caudimaculatus* stands guard to its eggs shedded to its side until they hatch but the single parent never misses a meal. The developing embryos are natural lures for would-be predators, which are then quickly devoured by the hungry father. This fin-on fatherhood species definitely gives his offspring a better chance of survival.

Shooting Anglerfishes

The best location to find frogfishes is Mabul Island, off Sabah, Malaysia. Though only three species are commonly found, if you are looking to see a football sized frogfish, this is the place. The hairy or striated frogfish can often be found in Secret Bay Bali or Lembeh Strait, North Sulawesi. Frogfishes are easily photographed, they don't move very much - if you can locate them that is.

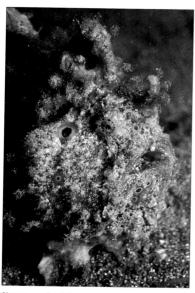

Shaggy anglerfish
Antennarius hispidus
6cm, Uncommon
Secret Bay, Bali, Indonesia
60mm f22 1/ 60sec

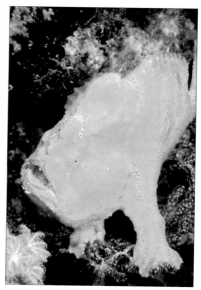

Painted anglerfish
Antennarius pictus
12cm, Commonly located
Mabul. Malaysia
60mm f16 1/60sec

Painted anglerfish
Antennarius pictus
10cm, Relatively common
Mabul, Malaysia
60mm f22 1/60sec

Getting to Know Seahorses & Pipefishes

There's an ethereal quality about seahorses that is difficult to resist. It is their aristocrat bearing, nobility, and bewitching stare that can freeze you momentarily. Well, fairy tales, myths or old wives tales, sea horses inspired our senses much more than any other marine animals. One of most recognizable of marine animals, with it distinctive features the seahorse has stimulated artists and writers for thousands of years. But few people know that the seahorse is really a fish, yes just like those with scales and fins. By some miraculous evolutionary technique, they evolved about 40 million years ago from a fish species similar to pipehorses, which in turn evolved from fish similar to pipefishes. Scientifically, they are classified in the genus of Hippocampus in the family of Syngnathidae, which includes the pipehorses, pipefish and sea dragons. To date there are 35 documented species worldwide varying in size from 2.5cm to 35cm.

Being an animal worthy of legends and bedtime stories, sea horses and their relative are different from the ordinary fish; they don't have scales but instead are encased in a series of bony plates under their skin, much like a suit of amour befitting a knight. The plates provide some form of protection from predators, but for some species they make their body semi-rigid. Their tail is prehensile, and their head spouts a long tubular snout supporting a toothless jaw enabling them to suck in small shellfish and larvae precociously. The head and foreparts are usually carried upright, resembling those of a horse. As such, seahorses and their relatives don't swim in a fish-like fashion, but glide gracefully, by fanning their small delicate fins supported by soft rays up to 70 times per second. Seahorses move very slowly. They are equipped with a prehensile tail; a useful contraption used to attached themselves to sea grass or just about anything within grasp to avoid being swept away by passing currents. In this aspect, Pipefishes, lacking this rigid quality, are thus confined to living in seaweed meadows or coral premises in sheltered bay like environments. The Syngnathidae family demonstrates a perceptible evolutionary gradient showing different degrees of specialization and changes. Pipefish are really a long skinny fish with a tubular mouth with small fins at the end of their rigid tail. Pipehorses are similar, with the exception of a slight prehensile tail without fins and a slightly bent head. The latest design, the most developed are the seahorses with head positioned at right angles to their body and tails which are specially design to grasp.

Because seahorses are slow swimmers, they rely on stealth for survival. Using their inconspicuous camouflage ability, seahorses can blend with their surroundings by growing tendrils and becoming shrouded with algae and encrusting organisms. Most ingeniously, some species can change colour to match their environ selectively. I have seen orange specimens living next to orange sponges, pink with pink sponges, green with sea grass and they are all of the same species.

Common seahorse
Hippocampus kuda
10cm, common
Mabul, Malaysia
60mm f22 11/125sec

Common seahorse
Hippocampus kuda
12cm, common
Secret Bay, Bali, Indonesia
60mm f22 1/60sec

Sargassum pipefish
Syngnathoides biaculeatus
15cm, Uncommon
Milne Bay, PNG
60mm f11 1/125sec

Pipefish are always there but rarely seen. Timid diurnal creatures and feeble swimmer they simply lay at the bottom well camouflaged, or float about either in caves or in the open, or hide in crevices or around wrecks. They use their elongated mouths like a pipette when feeding on small crustaceans, sucking in water which contains the prey with a quick forceful suction.

Eat or Be Eaten

Seahorses are picky eaters insisting on a diet of live crustaceans such as brine shrimp Despite their enchanting quality, seahorses are in fact voracious predators with their specialized long snout, which acts like a vacuum cleaner capable of sucking fast-moving shrimps out of the water column. An average sized seahorse is known to consume as many as 3000 brine shrimp per day. Pipefishes use their elongated mouths like a pipette quickly drawing in water and sediment and filtering out tiny crustaceans. They can move on prey very quickly. Although seahorses are easy to catch, they are not item of choice on the menu of other marine animals due to their bony unpalatable body. A fish would probably spit them out should one be taken by mistake. However, crabs and stingrays are not fussy eaters thus are the more formidable predators for seahorses.

In Bed with Seahorses & Pipefishes

In seahorse culture, they are staunch monogamists, mating exclusively with the same partner, literally to death do they part, but perhaps most outstandingly in seahorse society, it's the male that becomes pregnant. According to the leading seahorse observer and marine scientist, Amanda Vincent, they don't cheat and as far as her observation goes, they never get divorced either. Call them romantic if you will, but seahorses couple religiously performing a greeting dance every morning to confirm their bond. To procreate, the female deposits eggs into the male's brood pouch, where the male fertilizes them. Pipefishes are deprived of the specialized 'kangaroo' like pouch, thus eggs are attached to the outer surface of the male's tail. From then on, it is the male that carries the brood to term and does all the parenting. Astonishingly, the pregnant seahorse nature of care for the unborn young, resembles that of a human, providing nutrients and nourishment for between 21 days to 6 weeks for the pygmy seahorses. Studies confirm that the hormone prolactin, which stimulates milk production in women, also regulates seahorse pregnancy. Young seahorses are born live; little miniatures of the adults emerge from their father's pouch and are independent right from birth. Seahorses have a very low productive rate ranging from 200 to 20 eggs compared to the millions of other fish species. However, because of their specialized brooding process, juvenile seahorses have a better chance for survival in the wild. Unlike most other marine animals where their larvae are dispersed over a large area by surface currents, most seahorses are geographically unique. *Hippocampus fuscus* found only in tropical coast of Indian Ocean, *H. whitei* in East Australia, *H. breviceps* in South and East Australia, H. kuda is foun in Indonesia and Taiwan and *H. bargibanti* in PNG, Northern Australia and Indonesia. Male seahorses, almost immediately become pregnant again after giving birth.

ost of the seahorse species are listed by the Red list as vulnerable and may become
xtinct in the near future.   Countless numbers of seahorses are lost each year by our
estruction of coral reefs, mangroves and sea grass, beds. International trade statistics
ow that more than 20 million seahorses are mashed into Chinese medication annually.
everal million are sold in the aquarium trade, where the animals will surely die and tens of
ousands are turned into key chains and curios.   As they say, the Chinese are gullible,
lieving that seahorses cure everything from asthma, heart disease, lung cancer and
roat infections to lethargy but most significantly that they enhance libido. Reportedly,
ahorse populations in the world are collapsing.   At the current unrestricted
rvest,seahorses will definitely become extinct.   We all can help in protecting the
ahorses from extinction; discourage sea horse curios and the seahorse trade for
quariums.   Report any seahorse trade live or dead to: A. Vincent, Fax: 1 514
85069/:Amanda_Vincent@maclan.mcgill.ca

ngbanded pipefish - note the eggs on the male.
ryramphus dactyliophorus
m, common, Kelasey, Manado   60mm f22 1/125sec

Pygmy Seahorse
Hippocampus bargibanti
0.5cm, common in PNG &
Sulawesi, Eastern Indonesia
Lembeh Strait, Sulawesi
2:1 105mm f32 1/ 60sec

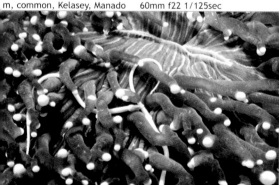

Mushroom coral pipefish
Siokunichthys nigrolineatus
3cm, Common
Alor, East Indonesia
60mm f16 1/60sec

Getting to Know SCORPIONFISHES

If anything in the fish world were to be compared to a creature from outer space it would have to be the diverse and bizarre family of Scorpiandae. The beauties and beasts of the reef, they range from the reds and flamboyant spiked wings of Firefishes (Pterois), to the grumpy face and monstrous appearance of Stonefishes (Synanceia). Small to medium sized, heavy-bodied fish they are usually less than 30cm(12in) in length. A family of diverse appearance from the huge ornate pectoral 'wings' of the commonly observed Lionfishes (Dendrochirus) and firefishes, to the dull mottled warty stonefishes. For this reason they have been divided into a number of sub-families, and have been given many common names such as Zebrafish, Turkeyfish, Butterflycod, and Waspfish, all evoking images of either danger or beauty.

Scorpionfishes get their name from their venomous spines. In some species they are more conspicuous than others, like the highly manoeuvrable spines of the dorsal fin of lionfishes. They have relatively large heads and large pectoral fins which are more like wings or fans. Lionfishes (Pterois & Dendrochirus sp.) have high cheekbones with a few spines, toady mouth and bulbous eyes high on the head.

Colour patterns vary from the bright reds, oranges, stripes and ornate plumage of the lionfishes, to the well camouflaged drab mottled hues of brown and green of the stonefish (Syanceia sp.). Some species in the Scorpaenopsis genus have additional leaf tassels, warts and bumps on their body coverings, and would certainly win no beauty contest. They are all artists of disguise. By growing additional appendages or producing mucous to stick on bits of algae to their body and laying semi-buried in silt, they are perfectly camouflaged from both their predators and prey. The scorpionfish family comprises of approximately 350 species and 70 genera and they are found mostly in Indo-Pacific waters.

Poisonous Prickles

All scorpionfish have potentially dangerous venomous spines positioned on their dorsal fins (sometimes also anal and pectoral fins). Under normal conditions they lay flat on the back and raised only as a defence mechanism when the fish is disturbed or harassed. Each spine is like a hypodermic needle connected to a venom sac at the base of the dorsal fin and ejects highly toxic venom into the intruder. The message simply is "Do not touch me!". Injuries can vary from the equivalent of a bee-sting, to a throbbing, or waves of excruciating pain. A wound from the deadly stonefish can result in paralysis, convulsions, unconsciousness, even cardiac and respiratory failure. Scorpionfishes are not aggressive. The onus is on the victim who might accidently step on, or press their hand on to a poor fish taking a nap on the reef bed. All scorpionfishes wounds should be immediately immersed in hot water, (as hot as you can stand). This will help alleviate the pain and dissolved the toxin.

Red firefish
Pterois volitans
28cm, Common
Mergui Archipelago Myanmar
60mm f11 1/125sec

Zebra lionfish
Dendrochirus zebra
22cm, Common
Davao, Phillippine
60mm f11 1/60sec

Two-eyed lionfish
Dendrochirus biocellatus
20cm, common in East Indonesia &PNG
Flores, Indonesia
60mm f11 1/60sec

Spotfin lionfish
Pterois antennata
18cm, Common
Maaya Thila, Maldives
60mm f11 1/60sec

Scorpionfishes

Domain of SCORPIONFISHES

Scorpionfish are solitary nocturnal predators that feed on crustaceans and small fishes. They lie on the reef bed or in caves and ledges and they are typically found in depths of 2-30m(6-100ft). While lionfishes are slightly more active at night roaming the reef in search of food, scorpionfishes remain almost stationary.

Eat or Be Eaten

They employ both ambush and decoy techniques to fish for dinner. Sitting patiently and motionlessly, they can take off in the speed of light to engulf passing fishes or crustaceans. We once witnessed a lionfish pounce by swiftly performing a 180 degrees turn to swallow a moving Basslet (Anthiinae).

Some species are opportunistic feeders. Sitting camouflaged on the bottom they will sometime engulf an innocent by-stander for an easy dinner.

In Bed with Scorpionfishes

Scorpionfish courtship begins after twilight. To win his mate for the evening the male sometimes has to engage in a brawl of head ramming with other potential suitors. Once successful he will don his courtship robe and patrol his territory for a female companion. When a female enters his courtyard, he swims and circles her, slowly positioning himself at her side. He then initiates the spawning by swimming a few feet off the bottom, and when fully aroused she will join him in his ascent to the surface to shed balls of thousands of floating eggs and sperm together. While the female descends to rest for the night, the male will hang around his lair to wait for another passing ripe female.

Shooting Scorpionfishes

Scorpionfishes are perfect portrait subjects! Shoot them any which way you can. Approach at your own pace (they move very slowly or not at all) and select their best profiles. They are full of facial expression with those lovely colorful tassels.

Lacy Scorpionfish
Rhinopias aphanes
23cm, Fairly rare
Milne Bay PNG
60mm f16 1/60sec

Bearded Scorpionfish
Scorpaenopsis cirrhosa
28cm, Common
Pulisan, Manado
60mm f11 1/ 60sec

Smallscale scorpionfish
Scorpaenopsis oxycephala
24cm,common
Tukang Besi, South Sulawesi
60mm f11, 1/125sec

Leaf scorpionfish
Taenianotus triacanthus
12cm, faily common
Nth. Halmerhera, Indonesia
60mm f11 1/ 60sec

Getting to Know GOATFISHES

The reef's equivalent of the terra firma animal grazing in the pasture is the Goatfish, often observed scavenging the reef bed for food. Its behaviour and facial expression often reminds us of that famous Manchurian gentleman, Fu Man Chu, with his curled up whiskers.

The most obvious features of the goatfish are the pair of "goats whiskers", otherwise called barbels, on its chin and the distinctively forked caudal fin. Other clues in the identification of this family include the two well separated dorsal fins and an elongated but solid body. Colouration ranges from the bright yellow striped goatfish to the iridescent pink and blue multi-bar species. They are medium sized fish, from 20cm up to 50cm for the largest member of the family. A small family consisting of about sixty species there are size differences between the sexes, the male or female being noticeably larger dependent on species type.

Domain of GOATFISHES

Though a few species of Goatfish prefer to hang out in schools, most of them are found probing along the sandy bottom of a reef individually or in small groups.

Eat or Be Eaten

Using their wriggling barbels as food detectors along the bottom they shift a lot of sand in one day in the search of their carnivorous diet of worms, crustaceans and small molluscs that live in the sediment. Goatfishes seem to have an insatiable appetite and bad eating habits. Pouncing sporadically upon some uncovered titbit they burrow their snouts into the sand leaving behind a cloud of sediment and crumbs. Of course other fishes such as the wrasse take advantage of the situation trailing along behind and freeloading off the leftover morsels.

Yellowfin goatfish
Mulloides vanicolensis
This is one of the few species
frequently found swimming in
school on top of reef top.
_21_cm, Common
Temple of Doom GBR, Australia
60mm f11 1/60sec

Doublebar goatfish
Parupeneus bifasciatus
_23_cm, Common coastal
Bunaken North Sulawesi
60mm f11 1/60sec

Yellowsaddle goatfish
Parupeneus cyclostomus
_29_cm, Fairly uncommon
Milne Bay, PNG
60mm f11 1/100sec

Goatfishes Mullidae

In Bed with Goatfishes

Goatfishes spawn in pairs and groups at the outer edge of the reef away from their normal feeding grounds. Within the conventional pair-spawning species, courtship behaviour is initiated by the male who patiently patrolls 3-6 ft (1-2m) above the reef awaiting the arrival of the female. When she arrives she approaches her suitor. Immediately the brief but fervent courtship follows with the male swimming around her in circles in an exaggerated display wriggling his barbels rapidly. When fully aroused the pair will dash to the surface together and release their gametes simultaneously.

Within the Group spawning species, the ritual begins with participating individuals from each pair approaching one another and swimming horizontally about 1m off the bottom. Others then join the pair converging into a group before dashing to the surface in unison for an explosion of gametes. The climax is over in seconds and the group disperses to join the other fish below. The floating fertilized eggs hatch after a few days but only settle to the bottom when they are between 40 and 60mm where they develop the characteristic barbels and change into the adult colours. Adulthood is said to be attained when they reach a length of 9-10cm.

Shooting GOATFISHES

We are able to get pretty close to Goatfishes. They are amazing to watch and they do not mind having a picture taken even of their ill-mannered eating habits. During the day scan the reef from about 2m (6 ft) off the bottom and you can easily spot a goatfish literally sweeping the reef bed. Approach gently and your subject would be quite oblivious of your presence and blinding effect of underwater strobes.

Some Goatfishes prefer to sleep out in the open and seem to have the ability to enhance highlights on their bright red, pink, yellow blue colours to warn off potential predators of the night. This is a great opportunity for portrait shots, where you can take your time to experiment with various camera angles and exposures.

Dash dot goatfish
Parupeneus barberinus
<u>23</u>cm, Common
anado, Murex, Nth. Sulawesi
60mm f11 1/60sec

Blackspot goatfish
Parupeneus signatus
<u>20</u>cm, Common coastal
Moyo, Indonesia
60mm f11 1/60sec

Red patch goatfish
Parupeneus heptacanthus
<u>27</u>cm, Fairly common
Ruang, Nth.Sulawesi
60mm f11 1/60sec

Getting to Know ANEMONEFISHES

The anemone fish is so called because of its special living arrangement amongst the stinging tentacles of sea anemones. Although part of the Damselfish family its symbiotic relationship with the anemone, bright colours, and clownish antics have earned it a special place in this book as well as the common name of clownfish.

Anemonefishes are easily recognizable, a common sighting, and fun to watch. They are found living in sea anemones where you will find them darting in and out of the tentacles of their host in a schizophrenic manner as if in a game of hide and seek.

Found in all tropical reefs from Red Sea to the Central Pacific there are 27 known species in the genus of Amphiprion, and 1 in the genus Premnas distinguished by one or two spines in the cheek. Anemonefishes are mostly brightly coloured as part of their effective defense mechanism to warn off predators. Typically one to three vertical white bars cross the body and in two species the bars are replaced by a white stripe running along the back from head to tail.

A courageous defender of its home the anemonefish is territorial in behaviour fearlessly charging the intruder no matter what their size but turning around at the last minute. An agitated or ill-tempered anemonefish may even ram an intruder or attack a scuba diver, or photographers' camera equipment. However the attack will result in nothing more than a nip or a pinch of the skin at worst.

With a life expectancy of at least 10 years they live in a social group, active during the day and sleeping at night amongst the folds of the anemone completely entangled in its tentacles.

Orangefin anemonefish
Amphiprion chrysopterus
, Common Western Pacific
Pohnpei, Micronesia
60mm f11 1/125sec

Eastern clownfish
Amphiprion percula
n, Common East Indonesia
Witu Island, PNG
60mm f16 1/60sec

da anemonefish with eggs
Amphiprion polmynus
_12_cm, localised Indonesia
Kelasey, Nth.Sulawesi
60mm f16 1/125sec

Domain of ANEMONEFISHES

Found at depths of 1-30m (2 -160ft) anemonefishes typically live together in a group on a single anemone and they are rarely seen away from their host. One of the most fascinating aspects of this small fish is its immunity to the anemones stinging cells (nematocysts), whose slightest touch would paralyze other fishes. These fish are not born with an in-built immunity system. They have to acquire it by picking up a substance from the mucus-coated tentacles that prevents the nematocyst from firing and the tentacles stinging each other. A newly born fish or one that has become separated from its host anemone for too long will have to acclimatize by rubbing itself against the tentacles to coat its body with the anemone's mucus. Once the gradual acclimatization is complete the anemonefish is fully immune to the sting and can spend unlimited time in the arms of its host - nature's way of ensuring a constant bond between fish and anemone.

Completely dependent on their landlord for protection an anemonefish will disappear quickly into its safe haven upon imminent danger. Within the relationship, the anemone is clearly seen as the 'big brother' offering the fish a home, protection, and even source of food. The benefit to the anemone is not so clear although it is said to enjoy the housecleaning provided by the fish. A 'clownfish' is never seen without an anemone, whilst an anemone can survive quite happily on its own.

Eat or Be Eaten

Feeding on zooplankton that floats past, the anemone itself also provides the fish with an additional food source. The anemonefish dines on the leftovers of food and algae on the anemone's tentacles and oral disk which might otherwise cause disease in its host, benefiting both host and tenant.

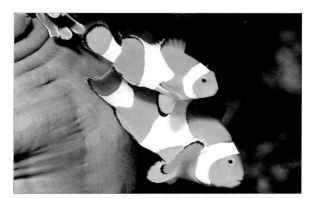

Common anemonefish
Amphiprion ocellaris
6cm, Common Indonesia
Bunaken, Nth Sulawesi
60mm f16 1/125sec

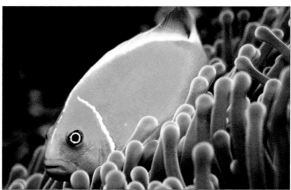

Pink clownfish
Amphiprion perideraion
n, Common West Pacific
Palau
60mm f16 1/125sec

Blackfooted anemonefish
Amphiprion nigripes
8cm, endemic Maldives
North Male Atoll,
60mm f16 1/60sec

In Bed with Anemonefishes

Anemonefishes live in a hierarchical social system. This is based on size and consists c the two largest adults at the top of the social ladder, of which the female is the larges and most socially dominant followed by the largest male, which is her partner for life All other fishes within the same household are male and smaller in size. In most case there is only one pair of adults to each anemone who permit other juveniles and smalle members of fish to co-exist with them.

One of the most intriguing things about the anemonefish is its ability to change sex Born hermaphrodites they have the ability to change sex when the appropriate time arrives. If the female anemonefish disappears or dies her male partner will change se over a couple of weeks, transforming into the female and assuming the leading role o the group. The next largest male will grow a little bigger and become her mate, wit each fish advancing one place in the hierarchy. This process can be amazingly reverse should the prodigal 'big mother' decide to have a change of heart and return home.

This practice is an efficient method of perpetuating their own species, allowing fish t find mates without leaving the protection of the home. The base of an anemone is safe haven for a nest and spawning, which takes place up to 13 times throughout the year. The courting process is initiated by the male who continuously bites at the tentacles of the anemone until they are withdrawn to reveal the nest site. The mal then leads the female to his lair and after bouts of body biting the trembling female starts laying between 300-500 eggs. He then swims over and fertilizes them. It is th male who performs the parental care by fanning the eggs to provide a steady flow c oxygen-rich water and defending them until they hatch in between 6-10 days. Hatchin usually just after sundown the microscopic offspring then float away. After 15 days c floating and growing the tiny juvenile fish are ready to bond with a host anemone an begin the process of acclimatization.

Shooting Anemonefishes

'Clownfish' are our favourite photographic subjects, but they are not co-operativ models. With lots of patience a great picture can be captured with a Nikonos and a 3: extension tube or a housed camera with 60mm lens. Do not try to chase the fish all ove the anemone, which might cause injuries to both its host, and the fish. With you framer or viewfinder, pick a section of the anemone to photograph and very quickly th fish will start to dart in and out of the frame. They have the habit of coming back to th same location.

Red & Black anemonefish
Amphiprion melanopus
ı, common East Australia
Sangie, Nth Sulawesi
60mm f16 1/125sec

Clarkii clownfish
Amphiprion clarkii
:m, Common Indo-Pacific
Kavieng, PNG
60mm f11 1/125sec

ɔinecheek - anemonefish
P*remnas biaculeatus*
2cm, widespread Pacific
Bunaken, Nth Sulawesi
60mm f16 1/60sec

Getting to Know HAWKFISHES

Though typically benthic, Hawkfishes do not bear the typical flattened, toady, or eel like characteristics. By contrast they have a stocky body with a marked half moon curve of the long and spiny dorsal fin capped by "cirri", resembling tassels. Along with the thickened pectoral fins of most floor dwellers all species have large green or black eyes rimmed with a ring of gold. Interesting colours and designs vary from the red cross hatch pattern of the Longnose Hawkfish (Oxycirrhites typus) and red freckled face o the Blackside Hawkfish to the Arc Eye Hawkfish with a red, yellow and white U-shape mark around its eyes. Other colour patterns include hues of orange and red horizonta bands to the drabber colours of rock camouflage. Generally a small fish of about 10cm (3"), species of up to 22.5cm(8") have been recorded (Randall 1990)

Domain of HAWKFISHES

Hawkfishes peacefully reside amongst hard coral, gorgonian fans, black tree coral and rocky substratums. Without a gas bladder, you will find Hawkfishes either hawking or top of a coral branch, or hopping along the reef bottom. With their thickened lower pectoral rays they wedge themselves among corals crevices to sleep at night. They are mainly found in tropical waters of the Indo Pacific (3 species are found in the Atlantic waters).

Eat of Be Eaten

Hawkfishes perch majestically on corals and rock shelves seemingly motionless and unmoved by a divers approach. Quiescent and patient, their 'hawk eyes' survey the ree for passing tiny fishes and crustaceans. When one is espied, the hawkfish will swiftly swoop and pounce upon its unsuspecting prey. It is this 'hawking' characteristic tha gives the carnivorous predator its common name.

Longnosed hawkfish
Oxycirrhites typus
:m, widespread Indo-Pacific
Pohnpei, Micronesia
60mm f16 1/125sec

Spotted hawkfish
Cirrhitichthys falco
m, widespread West Pacific
etak atoll, Marshall Islands
60mm f11 1/60sec

Freckled hawkfish
Paracirrhites forsteri
8cm, variation Indo-Pacific
Chuuk, Micronesia
60mm f16 1/125sec

In Bed with HAWKFISHES

Living in pairs or small groups these bold and fearless hunters have attributes of other such machismo reflected in their social set-up. In a male dominated society, hawkfish that live in groups comprise of one large male with several smaller females under his regime. The size of the harem varies according to the size of the territory, and may contain as many as 7 females in one coral head.

Hawkfishes spawn at dusk. The male, who has ignored his female companions all day starts by nudging and prodding his potential partners for that evening going from one female to another. Just before dark the willing females then move to a place on the corals sitting aloofly waiting for their 'man'. When he arrives he hops around the spawning site for a minute or so with his chosen mare before she suddenly stops and positions herself at the highest point with the male behind or beside her. There they sit in complete silence side by side for about 30 seconds presumably allowing the libido level to reach its peak. At the height of the crescendo, the pair then dash in unison into the water column releasing their gametes and eggs. On returning to the bottom the female then leaves the site and, if the male is lucky, he immediately moves on to the next female in the queue.

Shooting HAWKFISHES

Hawkfishes are perfect models. The magic is in their eyes and they are willing sitters for portrait photography. Approach them in a non-threatening fashion and you will usually find a willing model that performs various obliging poses as you fire away. Hawkfishes have been front cover models for advertising brochures, glossy magazines and coffee table books.

Arc-eye hawkfish
Paracirrhites arcatus
m, widespread Indo-Pacific
Bunaken, Indonesia
60mm f16 1/125sec

Spotted hawkfish
Cirrhitichthys falco
n, widespread West Pacific
GBR, Australia
60mm f11 1/60sec

Pixie hawkfish
Cirrhitichthys oxycephalus
8cm, variation Indo-Pacific
Bunaken, Nth Sulawesi
60mm f16 1/60sec

Sandperches Pinguipedidae

Getting to Know SANDPERCHES

Left to human imagination, we give names like sea cucumber to animals that are found slugging on the sea floor, and starfish to five armed animals that are not even a fish! Fishes of the family of Pinguipedidae or Mugiloididae family have a variety of imaginative names. In Australia they are called Whitings due to their main body colour, while in Africa they are called Sand Melts, probably because of their ability to bury themselves into the sand, and in many other English speaking countries they are called Sandperches or Grubfishes because they are found perching on or covered by sand. Then there is yet their other common name of Weaver, presumably inspired by their elaborate weaved body patterns.

There are more than 60 species of Sandperches in 4 genera but most of them are placed in the genus Parapercis. Some of them live in the deep sea but the reef dwellers are found perched on sand patches or rubble resting on their strong pelvic fins. Small slender cigar shaped fishes they have moderately compressed elongated bodies, sharp noses, and a terminal protractile mouth with canine teeth. They are frequently confused with Lizardfishes (Synodontidae). The difference between the two is the longer pointed snout and flatter head of the sandperch who often does not display his teeth.

Their body has a weaved pattern, typically of mottled brown, black or red on a white background and in some species males are distinguished from females by an additional dark marking on their head. (The male of the Sharpnose Sandperch {*Parapercis cylindrica*}has one or more dark markings on his head.)

Streaked sandperch
Parapercis stricticeps
<u>15</u>cm, Eastern Australia
Coral Sea Australia
60mm f11 1/125sec

Black banded sandperch
Parapercis tetracantha
widespread West Pacific
Alor, Indonesia
60mm f11 1/60sec

Multi-spotted sandperch
Parapercis multiplicata
<u>13</u>cm, East Indonesia
Milne Bay, PNG
105mm f11 1/60sec

Sandperches Pinguipedidae

Domain of SANDPERCHES

During the day they are found either resting on the reef floor propping themselves up with their pelvic fins or enjoying a hop all over the reef bed, occasionally stopping right in front of our cameras. They are territorial and on one dive trip we had repeated rendezvous over three days with the same four curious sandperches who we aptly named Nosey, Four-Eyes, Froggy and Grubby.

Eat or Be Eaten

Though occasionally small fishes are on their menu, they would rather feed on benthic crustaceans, especially small crabs and shrimps.

In Bed with SANDPERCHES

Sandperches live in a 'harem' environment. Their social system is based on a male defending his own territory and the territories of his harem of females. A Sharpnose Sandperch may defend a territory of about 17 square metres (56sqft) with his group of 2-5 females defending smaller areas against one another (Stroud 1981).

Mating is always within the harem, with the male selecting his companion for the evening at about 40 minutes before sunset. Moving side by side with his chosen partner he will boldly show his intentions by "bobbing" his head up and down in a mating dance. He may also place his head over her and arouse her by fanning her with his pectoral fins. With the right chemistry, the pair will rise in unison to about 60-70cm(27-32") off the bottom and release their sperms and eggs into the water column. The eggs are pelagic and the larvae wanders in the planktonic layer for about one to two months.

Shooting SANDPERCHES

Sandperches are a fish photographers delight. They have descriptive faces and they are easily photographed with a 60mm lens. For a great picture, shoot them at eye level.

Sharpnosed sandperch
Parapercis cylindrica
ɔ, Widespread West Pacific
Bitung. Nth Sulawesi
60mm f11 1/60 sec

Black tail sandperch
Parapercis. hexophthalma
7cm, common West Pacific
GBR, Australia
60mm f11 1/60sec

Belt sandperch
Parapercis signata
15cm, Indian Ocean
Ari Atoll, Maldives
60mm f11 1/60sec

Gobies Gobiidae

Getting to Know GOBIES

Gobies are the largest family of fishes known in the tropical ocean.

They are the smallest fishes in the reef and the tiniest vertebrates on earth. Even smaller than the fingernail of your little finger in some species, it is their small size and their large numbers that make them a major player in the ecology of coral reefs.

Being the largest family of fishes there are more than 1600 species documented, with about 200 genera, of which 1200 species inhabit the Indo-Pacific region. It is no wonder they are often mistaken for one another.

As might be expected of a huge family there are many variations in size, colour and shape. The tiniest Gobies may be less than 1cm (1/2") in length at adult size but within the family they rarely exceed 10cm(3"). Identification with such tiny subjects is difficult especially with so many closely related species. However distinct features that identify them from other small fishes, typically the Blenny family, are their elongated thin body with two distinct dorsal fins and scales. They have strong pectoral fins used not only for swimming and darting about, but when used in conjunction with their pelvic fin arrangements they appear to 'hop' around the sea bed. The pelvic fin is another distinguishing feature of the Gobies. Joined at the base it forms a shallow cup that acts as a "snowshoe" supporting the body weight on very soft sediments. This is particularly useful in surf-zone or in-shore species, as anyone who has tried to stay put in a big swell will understand.

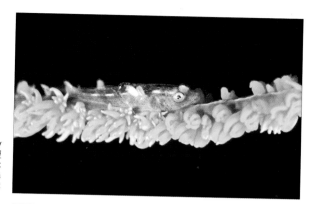

Whip Goby
Bryaninops yongei
2cm, Widespread Pacific
Sipadan, Malaysia
105mm f22 1/60 sec

Golden-headed goby
Valenciennea strigata
15cm, Widespread Pacific
Kelasey, Nth Sulawesi
60mm f11 1/60sec

Twin-spot goby
Signigobius biocellatus
Widespread West Pacific
Fiji
105mm f11 1/125sec

Gobies Gobiidae

Domain of GOBIES

Conservative, passive creatures and plodders by nature, the gobies are one of the few marine fishes who adopt a monogamous lifestyle in the conventional male and female relationship. Active during the day, typically you will see them in pairs (or alone) resting proudly at the entrance to their burrowed homes or scurrying about the bases of coral and rock.

The family homes of gobies are varied. There are species that love the open space and prefer to build their own home, hence they are found living in burrows out on the reef bed or hovering a short distance above it (some species do occur in congregation hovering in midwater). Other species may be found living in high rise apartment amongst hard coral plates, gorgonian fans, or hiding on the surface of sea whips or among gardens of soft corals. Some gobies are either translucent or match the camouflage colour of their habitat. Like most of us, some Gobies (e.g. Amblyeleotris, Cryptocentrus sp.) do not like housework. Many Indo-Pacific species have a shrimp as a live-in maid who works through the day keeping their burrow neat and tidy and free of loose rubble and sand.

While the maid performs its chores, the shrimp gobies guard the burrow at the entrance. At the first sign of danger the fish will dive into the burrow and cause the fortress to collapse. Once the Goby feels safe enough to return to the entrance the shrimp begins her housework all over again.

Eat or Be Eaten

The Arrow Goby of the U.S Pacific coast keeps a selection of labourers, from several species of worms and shrimp and sometimes the tiny pea-crab. The shrimp or pea-crab as usual does all the housework whilst the Goby goes out hunting for food. If at the end of the day if the fish has brought home morsels that are too large to swallow whole he may impose upon his shrimp maid to perform the duty of a domestic food processor. Undoubtedly shrimps or crabs are able to scavenge through the Goby's leftovers but it seems that the Gobies have a better deal in this relationship. Gobies display a wide range of diets, but most species are definite carnivores feeding mostly on tiny crabs or planktonic crustaceans. They may also eat molluscs, worms, sponges or the eggs of other fish or invertebrates and some species act as a cleaner fish scavenging the parasites from larger free-swimming pelagics.

Rain Goby
Amblygobius rainfordi
:m, Widespread West Pacific
Togian, Central Sulawesi
105mm f16 1/25 sec

Flag-tail shrimpgoby
Amblyeleotris sp.
living with alpheid shrimp
Alpheus randalli
13cm, Indonesia
Derawan, Indonesia
105mm f16 1/60sec

Steiners shrimpgoby
Amblyeleotris steinitzi
living with Alpheus bellutus
m, Widespread West Pacific
Bontang, Indonesia
105mm f11 1/125sec

Gobies Gobiidae

In Bed with GOBIES

Heterosexual pairs that form monogamous relationships have been documented for most gobies, although some appear to spawn randomly with either many individuals or a loosely organized group. In most species with the male playing the dominant role. He prepares the nest site by clearing the area on the roof of a small cave, underside of a shell, or their living burrow. Early in the morning he tries to entice the female to the nest by swimming back and forth between her and the nest site, typically in a display of exaggerated swimming and possibly nudging her on the snout to prompt some reaction. Up to one hour later after the commencement of courtship the female follows the courting male back to the nest to lay her eggs. Spawning occurs as both fish quiver frivolously side by side over the nest site, the male fertilizing each egg as she lays it. The number of demersal eggs produced depends on the species and size of female, but typically between 300-500 eggs are laid in one cluster. The eggs hatch in about 5-6 days and it is the male that performs the parental role of providing them with aerated water and protection.

Shooting GOBIES

Making pictures of Gobies teases your senses. They are small and they can be pretty quick. A 105mm lens is an essential. Attempting to take picture of the gobies and shrimp, a hasty approach will spook them to dive into their burrow. Once you have spotted your subject, stop about 3m(10 ft) in front of them. Frame them in your view finder and approach at a tortoise pace. As you draw closer, expend a few frames to accustom your model to the sound of your camera and flashes. Should they withdraw into their hide out, start all over again. Good pictures take time. For other gobies, it is important to observe their behavior and movement prior to shooting. This will enable you to select their best profile and backdrop for your shot.

Purple firegoby
Nemateleotris decora
n, Widespread West Pacific
in water beyond 25m
Fathers Reef,PNG
105mm f16 1/125 sec

Puntang goby
Exyrius puntang
possibly endemic
15cm, Jellyfish Lake
Kakaban, Indonesia
105mm f22 1/60sec

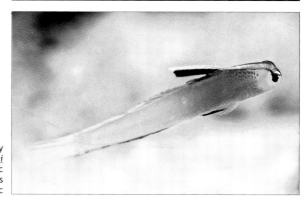

Pink firegoby
Nemateleotris helfrichi
n, uncommon West Pacific
Kwajalein, Marshall Islands
105mm f11 1/60sec

Getting to know BLENNIES

Blennies are some of the tiniest fish on the reef and often frequently mistaken for gobies. With a large fleshy cheek, frequently bulbous eyes and toady or froggy appearance they are affectionately described as cute. With over 270 species to their name they are bottom dwellers that inhabit the foreshore, reef flat and slopes of tropical and temperate waters. Being an odd-ball of the reef, Blennies are easily identifiable. There can be no excuse for mis-identifying a blenny for a goby. Blennies are blunt headed with their mouth situated low on their head and many have bizarre fringed or branched tentacles (cirri) protruding from their forehead. All Blennies are scaleless with one long continuous dorsal fin and their pelvic fins are clearly anterior to the pectoral fin. Apart from swimming and darting around, their strong pectoral fin arrangements are used for balancing on the reef. Some species that live on the inter-tidal zone are capable of leaping from rock pool to rock pool hence their given name of rock or mudskipper (eg. Entomacrodus sp.).

Domain of BLENNIES

Unlike Gobies who build their own burrows and enjoy monogamous relationships, Blennies prefer to adopt a bohemian singular lifestyle with little time for domesticity. Found in depths of up to 25m (80 feet) they live in coral crevices and holes and they will only build a nest if there are women to entice. Their hideouts are usually small which they have the habit of entering backwards and tail first. In the day, blennies can either be located watching the world go by from inside their quarters or perching on their front doorstep.

Eat or Be Eaten

Though most of the tropical species are herbivorous, some feed on coral polyps and small crustaceans as well as zooplankton and eggs of other fishes. A few of their members however, give the blenny family a bad reputation. The Sabretooth Blennies (*Plagiotemus* and *Aspidontus spp.*) are prime examples. Being of similar colouration to the cleaner wrasse (*Labroides dimidiatus*), they are able to mimic the harmless cleaner wrasse to get closer to their prey. Having fooled its unsuspecting prey it then uses two enormous canine teeth in its lower jaw to attack the fish, feeding on its scales, mucus and dermal tissues. Other Blennies have jumped onto the mimicing habits of their sabretooth cousins. The Lyre-tail or Cleopatra Eye Blenny (*Meiacanthus sp.*) is the boldest of the family and is equipped with venomous fangs for defence purposes. It is no wonder that they feel bold enough to hover way off the bottom as predators have learnt to avoid them. Other 'copycat' species, including Plagiotremus, Petroscirtes, and Ecsenius spp., may also impersonate this venomous fanged species to deceive other predators.

Bath's comb-tooth
Ecsenius bathi
4cm, variation to area
Banda, Indonesia
105mm f16 1/60 sec

White-spot combtooth
Ecsenius trilineatus
n, Indo-Pacific to Solomon
Sorong, Indonesia
105mm f16 1/125 sec

Bath comb-tooth
Ecsenius bathi
4cm, variation to area
Bunaken, Nth. Sulawesi
105mm f16 1/60 sec

In Bed with Blennies

Contrary to the traditional traits, in Blenny society it is the female that initiates courtship but the male that provides the maternal duties of tending and defending eggs.

Spawning activity varies with species but always occurs during the day at some stage and takes place near the male domain. The female in her courtship colours begins the process by passing in front of the male lair. In some species the male might swim towards the female in an up and down sinussoidal motion while in other species the male will just pose at the entrance of his hole and perform the Blenny Courtship rite of 'head bobbing' (shaking his head vigorously up and down).

Once the male feels that he has successfully aroused his partner he will try to lead her to his nest or sit in front and signal her towards it whilst continuing to 'bob' his head. Subject to a satisfactory inspection of his den, she then parks herself (bottom first) into it and lays her eggs. If the site is large enough the male will sit side by side undulating with her in unison; as she lays her eggs he fertilizes them. Otherwise he sits outside to drive away any intruder still 'bobbing' and pops back in to fertilize the eggs at regular intervals. The process lasts from a few minutes to half a day in some species, producing between 100 - 160 eggs (Fishelson 1975). The female Orange Spotted Blenny (*Exallias brevis*) spawns regularly every three to four days, producing an average of 200,000 - 300,000 eggs per year. The demersal eggs are generally large and hatch in about nine days with the male aerating them vigorously during hatching time.

Shooting Blennies

I love Blennies, sometimes having spent up to four hours trying to take a picture of pregnant Banded Blenny. This little super intelligent trickster seems to have the aptitude to pre-empt every move, confounding me with an artful routine of disappearing acts. Even with a pre-focusing technique, they will sit still long enough for composition but retreat into their hole just as you are about to depress the shutter. To outwit blennies, I carry an extra camera with lots of film. Patience is a pre-requisite and do not be surprised if you resort to praying and talking to the little monster.

Mimic cleaner blenny
Aspidontus taeniatus
1, widespread Indo-Pacific
Kwajalein, Marshall Island
105mm f16 1/125 sec

Blue-stripped fangblenny
agiotremus rhinorhynchos
cm, Indo-Pacific Common
Bunaken, Indonesia
105mm f16 1/125 sec

Piano fangblenny
lagiotremus tapeinosoma
10cm, uncommon
Davao, Phillippines
105mm f16 1/125 sec

Bicolor blenny
Ecsenius bicolor
4cm, Indo-Pacific- variat
Sipadan, Malaysia
105mm f16 1/125 sec

Meia fangblenny
Meiacanthus species
10cm, uncommon
Kimbe Bay, PNG
105mm f11 1/60 sec

Leopard blenny
Exallias brevis
m, widespread Indo-Pacific
Bunaken, Nth Sulawesi
105mm f16 1/60 sec

Banded blenny
Salarias fasciatus
15cm, West Pacific
Witu Island, PNG
105mm f16 1/60 sec

Cleopatra-eyes lenny
Meiacanthus atrodorsalis
6cm, Common
GBR, Australia
105mm f11 1/125 sec

Dragonets Callionymidae

Getting to Know Dragonets

Dragonets are adorable but bad smelling fish; instead of scales these small fishes with broad cheeky heads opt for a tough slimy skin which tastes bad and smells bad, thus the common name of stink fish. The skin's mucus coating not only offers protection to the body but also effectively wards of parasites and skin diseases. However foul smelling they may be, dragonets are absolutely fabulous and easy to love. Their mouth is noticeably protruded, extending out in a downward angle and their dorsal fins are comprised of separate spiny and soft parts.

Over 125 species in 9 genera are known in the Indo-Pacific Ocean. Dragonets are one of the few marine fishes that can be easily sexed, which makes it easy to distinguish between the boys and girls. The males are heavily built and may attain a whopping size of 6cm. The caudal and soft dorsal fins are larger in the male and the most distinctive difference is that the males have an exaggeratedly elongated first dorsal spine while females do not.

The most prominent of the species is the *Synchiropus splendidus*, or the Mandarinfish, though cryptic to the untrained observer it is probably one of the most distinctive fish of the tropical reef. Few other fishes can match its startling combination of unusual shape and remarkable colouration. With such incredible beauty *S. Splendidus* is said to be a 'must see' fish before one expires from this planet - the highest accolade ever bestowed on a bony vertebrata. Uncountable passionate naturalists have anecdotally fallen in love at first sight with cacophonies of 'wow's and 'ooh's. Mandarinfish are predominantly satin-green to blue with striking orange wavy lines bordered with hues of orange, green, purple and yellow. The somewhat bizarre colour patterns have to be seen to be believed.

Domain of Dragonets

Though dragonets are diurnal fishes, they are rarely seen in the open during the day. They are benthic, often buried in sand bottoms or hiding in coral outcrops, and they move along hugging the substrate closely, virtually skipping from cover to cover.

Eat or Be Eaten

Typical of tiny bottom dwellers with a refined gastronomical habit, dragonets are pretty picky with their choice of food. With a small pointed mouth they prefer to feed on small fresh morsels of crustaceans such as Mysids, amphipods, isopods, benthic copepods, small worms and protozoans.

Mandarinfish
Synchiropus splendidus
, Widespread /uncommon
Kapalai, Malaysia
105mm f22 1/125sec

Dragonet species
Undescribed
2cm, Uncommon
Manado Tua, Nth Sulawesi
105mm f22 1/60sec

Fingered dragonet
Dactylopus dactylopus
15cm, widespread
nbeh Strait, Nth Sulawesi
105mm f16 1/125sec

In Bed with Dragonets

The best time to see dragonets is the hour before the sun retreats beyond the horizon; this is whoopee time for dragonets. In human terms, it is much like Happy Hours at water holes or Pubs, where opportunistic males also hang out in the evening to search for willing females.

As on nature's biological clock, at dusk, dragonets reveal themselves from their shelter. Males begin to flash themselves by erecting their stunning dorsal fin at females in passing. Once a female has selected her partner for the evening, she will simply go up to her suitor, give him a kiss on the cheek seemingly to say, you are the one I want NOW. The male readily pairs with the female, cheek to cheek, buttocks touching buttocks, fins holding fins they began to rise off the bottom. As they rise, their fins exaggeratedly flutter in unison, their tiny faces radiating excitement and satisfaction. When they reach the peak of their communion, eggs and sperm are simultaneously shed and literally in a flash, the pair disperse their separate ways. Neither guilt nor obligation nor politeness is necessary; a union solely for the sake of individual relief and procreation of the species without commitment.

If you are wondering about the parental care, dragonets have the scheme all figured out; eggs are hatched in 18 hours in the water column, and two weeks of orientation in the planktonic zone prepares dragonet larvae for a lifetime in a footloose and fancy free environment. Dragonets such as the Mandarinfish are said to be hypersexed, thus known to mate every night of the year.

Shooting Mandarinfishes

Pun fully intended, when you are hot, you are hot and as the aphorism goes, experience with sex gets better with practice. I bumped into Bert Yates, David Doubilet's sidekick in Micronesia and he graciously showed me the way to the 'King Cross' of the specie. Apart from the orthodox sessions, we saw an atypical sexual behavior of Mandarinfish; two males and a female reaching apex seven times in succession. We were the first to watch such an encounter and the first to capture the sequence on film I was later told. Best place to photograph them Kapalai (Sabah Malaysia, Lembeh Strait, North Sulawesi, Secret Bay, Bali and Palau.)

Mandarinfish
Synchiropus splendidus
first time ever observed
threesome mating sequence
Palau
105mm f22 1/60sec

Getting to Know Flounders & Soles

Flounders and Soles are the flatfishes of the reef, with distinctive, prominent distinguishable characteristics; they both have a blind side that is the side with no eyes, while on the other side they have two eyes. As flat-bodied animals, orientation can be difficult, causing them to live on the sand with their eye side up and blind side down. They move or swim on their blind side.

Through the course of 65 million years, some of their ancestors decided to have both their eyes on the left while some decide to have them on the right thus taxonomists obliged with a classification of right-eyed flounders - the family Pleuronectidae and the left-eyed group, the family Bothidea. Generally the common flounders in the Indo Pacific tropical waters are left-eyed with the exception of few. The family of flounders is large by fish standards with over 300 species, but only 90 species in 15 genera are found in the tropical waters.

They are extremely compressed, with the ocular side (the side with eyes) pigmented to match their surroundings. Among fishes, they are masters of their domain, the "chameleon of fishes", possessing ability to modify pigmentation pattern to mimic the environment exactly. They often cover their body with a fine layer of sand and stay immobile for a long periods of time with only their protruding eyes probing the environ like a periscope for prey and predators. Among the species, the pigmentation pattern of the eye side varies extensively but the blind side is usually pale or un-pigmented. Common species of flounders are the Peacock flounder (*Bothus mancus*) and Leopard flounder (*Bothus pantherinus*), both capable of attaining 45 cm and 35 cm respectively.

Determined not to be mistaken, all soles in the tropics are right-eyed, comprising of 100 species in 30 genera. However, it is believed they have been poorly described and much scientific work is required to redefine the Soleidae family. The right or ocular side of sole is striped or patterned, while the underside is un-pigmented. Soles are smaller fishes, with asymmetrical features in addition to eye orientation; small eyes, a small twisted mouth with small teeth, small head with fins comprised almost entirely of soft rays surrounding body outline, except the head, ventrally. As such, they are worm-like when they move along the bottom. In addition, some soles have a snorkel or a long hook on the snout that overhangs the mouth region.

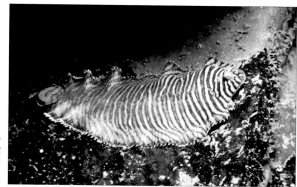

Zebra sole
Zebrias zebra
7cm, uncommon
Witu Island, PNG
105mm f22 1/60sec

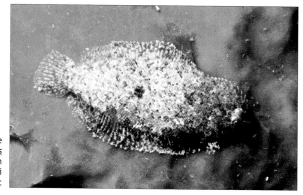

Black spotted sole
ardachirus melanospilos
*10*cm,Sulawesi/ Ambon
anado Tua, Nth Sulawesi
105mm f22 1/60sec

Heter sole
Soleichthys heterohinos
*12*cm, rare
Maaya Thila, Maldives
105mm f16 1/60sec

Domain of Flounders & Soles

Flounders and soles don't really live on the reefs, but on sandy slopes or mud bottoms. As benthic animals, with mouth and eyes on the top, they are biologically designed to feed on small fishes and invertebrates from the reef floor. Most of them are active at dawn and dusk, but mostly nocturnal. There are few diurnal species.

In Bed with Flounders & Soles

One would imagine sex among flatfishes to be pretty compressed, but the truth is there have been very few observations among the species. However, they surely lay eggs and after hatching in the planktonic zone. The larval fish has the general features and behavior of a symmetrical fish. As they develop however, one eye will begin a slow dramatic sojourn across the top of the head towards the other side of the body to say hello to the other eye. By now the deformed Picasso-like fish will settle on its blind side on the ocean floor.

Shooting Flounders & Soles

Stare hard enough, sands will quiver and behold in front of you will be a Peacock flounder and the best time to find them is at dusk or dawn. They are easily approached and a delight to photograph. One of my favorites is the Blue-edge sole (*Soleichthys heterohinos*), I found in the Wita Islands, PNG and Maaya Thila, Maldives.

Peacock flounder
Bothus mancus
35cm, widespread common
Bunaken, Nth Sulawesi
60mm f22 1/125sec

Leopard flounder
Bothus pantherinus
_30_cm,common
Layang Layang, Malaysia
60mm f22 1/125sec

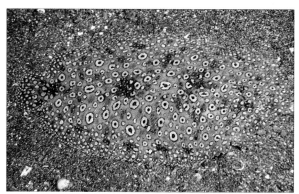

Peacock sole
Pardachirus pavoninus
_22_cm,West Pacific
Lembeh Strait, Nth Sulawesi
60mm f16 1/60sec

Porcupinefishes Diodontidae

Getting to Know PORCUPINEFISHES

Looking at the Porcupinefish it is easy to see where this short, rotund, rather comical character derives its name. Commonly known as the balloonfish, burrfish or spiny puffer it is easily identifiable by the spines covering its head and body and one of the only fish families that can be seen slowly waddling, rather than swimming through the water. A Porcupinefish has the unique ability to inflate itself into a ball shape by filling its abdomen with water when danger threatens. It has an extra advantage over its cousin, the pufferfish. When inflating itself, sharp spines point outwards as an additional deterrent against would be predators. With this effective defense system they do not need to be good or fast swimmers and appear to waddle along in a rather funny fashion, propelling themselves with their soft dorsal and anal fins. Apart from their spines they differ from the puffers in appearance by having larger eyes, broader more pronounced pectoral fins and generally do not have the complex patterns. Despite their effective armour of spines they are passive in nature, coexisting quite happily minding their own business with little or no aggression. When pushed or tormented however be warned, they are capable of inflicting a severe bite. Found in both tropical and temperate seas there are about 19 species in this family of small to medium size fish. The larger oceanic fishes like marlin, sharks and tunas feed on juvenile porcupinefishes often at their own peril. We once found a dead 8 ft marlin with an inflated porcupine stuck in its throat. Found at the reef bottom up to depths of 30m (100ft) or more these timid fishes usually lead a solitary life. Many are nocturnal, retiring into caves, hiding beneath ledges, or hovering quietly in some sheltered area during the day.

Opportunistic predators, they feed on a varied diet of organisms at the bottom. Using their shearing teeth and powerful jaws they crush the shells from their staple diet of sea urchins, molluscs, crabs, hermit crabs and snails to feed on the soft tissues inside.

In Bed with Porcupinefishes...very carefully

Porcupinefish spawn in pairs or in a group of several males to one female. The male starts the courtship by following the female initially, occasionally gently nudging her abdomen. After a while, if she is receptive to his advances, she then ascends further off the bottom with the male trailing behind. When sufficiently aroused, the mating process becomes a little rougher as the male pushes the female to the surface by pressing his snout against her abdomen, where she sheds her eggs as he releases his sperm. They then rush back to the bottom leaving the eggs to hatch. Their offspring spend some time floating as planktonic larvae before settling to the bottom.

Shooting Porcupinefishes

They are slow swimmers, this does not mean that you should deliberately catch one to take a picture of an inflated balloon. It is a pretty un-cool thing to do and the fish won't be too keen on the idea either! When one is spotted, simply observe their swimming path and position yourself along it to catch your portrait shot.

Rounded porcupinefish
Cyclichthys orbicularis
21cm, Indo-Pacific
Komodo, Indonesia
60mm f11, 1/125sec

Fine-spotted porcupinefish
Diodon holocanthus
m, circumtropical/temperate
Kelasey, Nth Sulawesi
60mm f11 1/125sec

Masked porcupinefish
Diodon liturosus
*45*cm, Indo-Pacific
may be found swimming
at reef edge.
Sipadan, Malaysia
60mm f11 1/60sec

ropical Reef Life

e companion to Tropical Reef Fishes; an authoritative
verage on tropical reef invertebrates from corals,
emones, sponges, crustaceans, mollusks, worms,
lls to sea stars. A handy identification and natural
tory guide for nature lovers, scuba divers, snorkellers,
dents and underwater photographers. Illustrated with
r 500 new images captured in the wild. Colour coded
easy reference. For photographers, tips and 'how to's
capturing better images, with lens and exposure
ormation included for every photograph.

Raves

avel guide to the exotic and bizarre life forms of the tropical
f by one of the world's leading underwater photographers.
rles Darwin meets 'Melrose Place'! A reference guide
bining skillful measures of scientific observation with
ertaining fact. - David Strike, Editor of Professional Diver
rnal (Australia) A$ 20 / US $15

nited edition / autographed copy
$55

"24 Hour Beneath a Rainbow Sea" is
unique, the almanac is a documentary of a day
in the life of a submerged reef system as seen
through the eyes of the 24-hour dive team. All
the images are actually captured between 10 to
11 April 1999. The energy and enchantment of a
marine reserve in the Maldives is beautifully
revealed in a celebration of artistic imagery.
Learn the intricacies and idiosyncrasies of
sharks, octopus, eels, snappers, turtles,
clownfish and their neighbourhood of critters.
Relive the 24-hour odyssey in a metropolis of
marine animals and indulge in the glory and
colours of Planet Earth's rainbow realm. A " Gift
of State" high quality limited edition

Ocean Portraits Book

igh quality ready to frame 10" x12" prints of reef fishes and dolphins. Award Winning
ges.
 Gift screen saver WIN 95/98/2000 of all the images. A$25 /
0

rder any of the above fax or e-mail with name, address,
e/fax number, e-mail. Payment by bank cheque or VISA /
er cards.
de expiry date and billing address. Postage not included.
anNEnvironment
 61 2 9686 3688
il:oneocean@OceanNEnvironment.com.au
.OceanNEnvironment.com.au

About the Author

Michael AW is a photojournalist based in Sydney, he specialises in wildlife, environmental and travel features. His articles and photographs have been featured in publications spanning from Australia, Asia, Europe to the USA, including, Times, Asian Geographic, NATURE Focus, GEO, Ocean Realm, Scuba Diver, Action Asia and Sojourn. His photographs have won many national and international awards including the Nikon International Photographic competition. He has presented lectures at DEMA, international aquariums, as well as to The Australian Museum Society.

Michael & his wife Alison Redhead are the principals of OceanNEnvironment, a non-profit public company dedicated to preserve the quality of the marine environment.

Mandarinfish - group mating behavoir

Other Titles by the Same Author
Beneath Bunaken
Tropical Reef Life
METAMORPHOSEA
Dreams from a Rainbow Sea Maldives
OneOcean Portrait

Acknowledgement
Without the support of the dive and travel operators, this book will not be possible. My heart felt thanks to all for gracious assistance and generosity. Dr. Hanny Batuna, Chris Taylor, Tono, Robert Lo, Nicole Lenoir-Jourdan, Agisa Abdullah, Raymond Howe, Matthew Hedrick, Seno and John Bagus to name but a few. I also wish to thank all my lovely assistants for caddying extra cameras for me Heather Brown, Barbara Evans, Heather Halloran and especially my wife Alison..you all have made each dive much more enjoyable & productive. Special thanks to Ike Brigham and Larry Ostendorf of Ikelite for giving lights to my pictures. Special thanks also to Gerry Allen and Robert Myers for assisting with identification. Once again my appreciation to my long time friend, Sidney Seok for helping unconditionally. Also thanks to Merridy Cairn-Duff for sorting out the text. To all that have helped, who we have inadvertently omitted to mention, our deepest thanks. God Bless.